WJEC/Eduqas

Geography

Glaciated landscapes

Tectonic hazards

Sue Warn

Hodder Education, an Hachette UK company, Blenheim Court, George Street, Banbury, Oxfordshire OX16 5BH

Orders

Bookpoint Ltd, 130 Park Drive, Milton Park, Abingdon, Oxfordshire OX14 4SB

tel: 01235 827827

fax: 01235 400401

e-mail: education@bookpoint.co.uk

Lines are open 9.00 a.m.–5.00 p.m., Monday to Saturday, with a 24-hour message answering service. You can also order through the Hodder Education website: www.hoddereducation.co.uk

ISBN 978-1-4718-9950-8

First printed 2017

Impression number 5 4 3 2 1

Year 2018 2019 2018 2017

This guide has been written specifically to support students preparing for the WJEC/Eduqas AS and A-level Geography examinations. The content has been neither approved nor endorsed by WJEC/Eduqas and remains the sole responsibility of the author.

Cover photo: dabldy/Fotolia; map on p. 104 redrawn from NOAA/Center for Tsunami Research data.

Typeset by Integra Software Services Pvt. Ltd, Pondicherry, India

Printed in Italy

Contents

Content Guidance

Glaciated landscapes

Tectonic hazards

Questions & Answers

Getting the most from this book

Exam tips

Advice on key points in the text to help you learn and recall content, avoid pitfalls, and polish your exam technique in order to boost your grade.

Knowledge check

Rapid-fire questions throughout the Content Guidance section to check your understanding.

Knowledge check answers

1 Turn to the back of the book for the Knowledge check answers.

Summaries

- Each core topic is rounded off by a bullet-list summary for quick-check reference of what you need to know.

Exam-style questions

Commentary on the questions

Tips on what you need to do to gain full marks, indicated by the icon ⓔ

Sample student answers

Practise the questions, then look at the student answers that follow.

Commentary on sample student answers

Read the comments (preceded by the icon ⓔ) showing how many marks each answer would be awarded in the exam and exactly where marks are gained or lost.

Tectonic hazards

(i) Study the map. Describe the temporal impact of this event across the Indian Ocean. (6 marks AO3)

ⓔ This question follows the format of Eduqas AS questions. This is a skills-based question so it relies on your accurate interpretation of the map.

Student answer

The zone of fault rupture (epicentre) was from the Sumatra earthquake at the Sunda trench giving no warning to Aceh in Indonesia ✓. After 2 hours the wave had spread to Sri Lanka and southern Sumatra and Thailand ✓. Progress was much more rapid across the open waters of the Indian Ocean than to Java and northern Sumatra ✓. After 5 hours impacts had spread to the west coast of India and northwest Australia ✓. By 7–8 hours the waves had reached to the Somali coast and the southern Australia coast ✓. It is noteworthy that places such as Borneo and Brunei, much nearer, were reached at the same time as Antarctica ✓. The last places to feel the impact, some 24 hours later, included the Gulf of Thailand and northeast Australia — so there is not a clear correlation to distance ✓. Coastal configuration is clearly important as well as the degree of open water for the wave to move across ✓.

ⓔ The marks are awarded in three bands based on the detail of description and the thoroughness of resource use.

Band 3: 5–6 marks

Band 2: 3–4 marks

Band 1: 1–2 marks

This answer achieves the maximum 6 marks for accurate analysis of the resource.

(a) (ii) Look at the table below. Suggest and justify a statistical technique you could use to correlate the arrival time of the tsunami with the number of deaths. (4 marks)

Human impacts of the Boxing Day tsunami

	Indonesia	Burma (Myanmar)	India	Maldives	Sri Lanka	Thailand
Deaths	169,000	81	10,750	81	31,000	5,300 (including 2,248 foreign nationals)
Missing	150,000+	1	5,550	n/a	4,000	2,800
Homes damaged or destroyed	200,100	5,000	15,000	15,000	100,000	60,000+
People displaced (some in relief camps)	600,000	10,000–15,000	140,000	11,500	500,000	300,000 (Burmese migrants a real problem)
Total population	217,500,000	48,956,000	1,041,410,000	309,000	19,287,000	64,340,000

Source: Geo Factsheet Number 194, www.curriculum-press.co.uk

Glaciated landscapes; Tectonic hazards 105

About this book

Much of the knowledge and understanding needed for AS and A-level geography builds on what you have learned for GCSE Geography but with an added focus on theories, geographical skills and techniques, and the specialised concepts listed in the specification.

This guide has two sections:

- The **Content Guidance** summarises the key information that you need to know to be able to answer the examination questions on glaciated landscapes and tectonic hazards with accuracy and depth. In particular, the meaning of key terms is made clear. You will also benefit from noting the exam tips, which provide further help in determining how to learn key aspects of the course. Knowledge check questions are designed to check your depth of knowledge.
- The **Questions & Answers** section includes sample questions similar in style to those you might expect in the exam. There are sample student responses to these questions as well as detailed commentary giving further guidance in relation to what exam markers are looking for in order to award top marks. The best way to use this book is to read through the relevant topic area first before practising the questions. Only refer to the answers and comments after you have attempted the questions.

The topics covered in this guide are:

WJEC AS Unit 1 Changing landscapes

- Section A Changing landscapes: Glaciated landscapes
- Section B Tectonic hazards

WJEC A2 Unit 4 Contemporary themes in geography

- Section A Tectonic hazards

Eduqas AS Component 1 Changing landscapes

- Section A Changing landscapes: Glaciated landscapes
- Section B Tectonic hazards

Eduqas A-level Component 1 Changing landscapes and changing places

- Section A Changing landscapes: Glaciated landscapes

Eduqas A-level Component 3 Contemporary themes in geography

- Section A Tectonic hazards

Content Guidance

Glaciated landscapes

The operation of a glacier as a system

Formation of glacier ice

Glacier ice is formed primarily from compacted snow, with smaller contributions from other forms of precipitation such as hail or sleet which freeze directly on top of or inside the glacier.

Granular snow (density 0.19 cm^{-3}) is increasingly compacted to form **névé** or **firn**. Further pressure transforms firn into glacier ice (density 0.9 cm^{-3}), which is then deformed by further pressure to flow outward (in the case of an ice sheet/cap) or downward (for a glacier) by **extrusion flow**.

- From snowflake to firn can take a few days (in temperate areas), but is much slower (10 years) in polar areas.
- The final stage from firn to glacier ice may take 25 years in temperate areas but up to 150 years in polar areas.
- Overall rates of transformation from snow to ice can be as little as 100 years in some temperate areas, but can take up to 4000 years in Antarctica.

Knowledge check 1

Define the term 'firn'.

Inputs and outputs of the glacier system

Glaciers can be viewed as open systems, with inputs, outputs and interactions with other systems such as the atmosphere, oceans, hydrosphere and landscape. Within systems there are various stores, in this case the glaciers and other ice masses, and energy and materials are transferred by flows/fluxes.

The glacier system is driven by inputs of energy from the sun, which evaporates water from the oceans to create air masses. These can produce precipitation (snowfall, sleet and hail). Mass enters the system in the form of snowfall and rock debris (inputs). As this mass generally occupies an elevated position in the Earth's gravitational field, this mass has **potential energy** which is expended as the glacier flows downslope. The energy expended is used to warm or melt ice, and then must be dissipated from the system in the form of heat and water (outputs). As this is going on, potential energy is turned into work, transferring ice and rock from highland areas towards lower levels and the oceans.

Exam tip

A study of systems is a vital part of the specification. Learn the key diagram (Figure 1).

Knowledge check 2

Explain why glaciers can be viewed as **open** systems.

Glacier mass balance

Mass balance is defined as the gains and losses of the ice store in the glacier system.

Accumulation results from direct snowfall or other precipitation, and from icefalls, blown snow and avalanching from slopes above the glacier surface.

The snow and ice are then transferred down-valley by glacier movement until they reach lower areas where they are lost to the system by processes collectively known as **ablation**.

Ablation results from melting, evaporation (sublimation) or the breakaway of ice blocks and icebergs at sea level (known as **calving**).

At the same time, there is input of rock debris supplied by weathering and erosion of slopes above the glacier. This is transported and eventually deposited as another glacier output in the form of moraines and other deposits.

As Figure 1 shows:

- there is more accumulation than ablation in the upper part of the glacier
- there is more ablation than accumulation in the lower part of the glacier
- the glacier's **equilibrium point** is where accumulation and ablation balance each other out

Glaciers are dynamic systems as the ratios of inputs to outputs vary considerably between glaciers, and continually over both short-term and longer-term timescales.

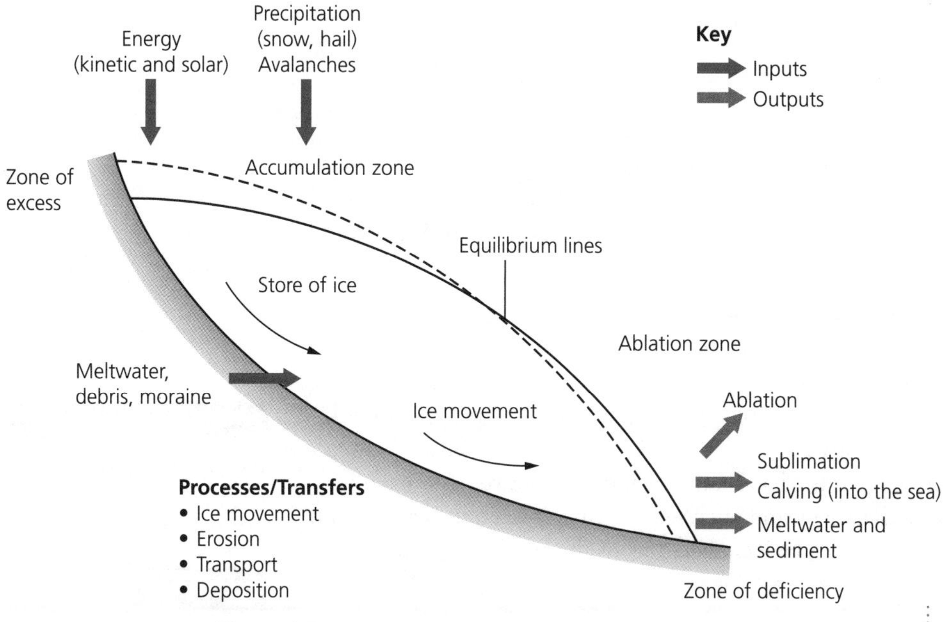

Figure 1 The glacier mass balance as a system

Short-term changes

Figure 2 shows the following theoretically.

- If accumulation exceeds ablation, the usual situation during the winter, the glacier increases in mass, i.e. a **positive regime** for the glacier budget. This causes the glacier to grow and therefore to **advance** at the snout.

- Conversely, in summer when there is more ablation than accumulation (because of rising temperatures), the glacier budget has a **negative regime**. This causes the glacier to shrink, thin or **down waste**, and therefore the snout begins to retreat.
- If the annual **net** balance is zero, i.e. there is no difference between accumulation and ablation, in theory the glacier is likely to be at a **stillstand**.
- Even within the timespan of the annual budget, the changing regimes (which cause changes in annual net balances) are likely to have some visual impact on the size of the glacier mass.

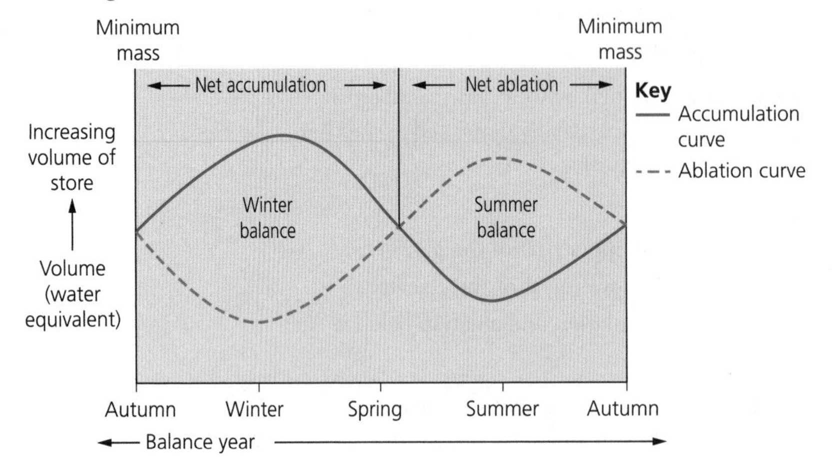

Figure 2 A model of the annual mass balance of a typical glacier. Note: the mass balance year runs from autumn to autumn when ice masses are generally at their lowest volume

Longer-term changes

In the longer term the situation is far more complex. The annual net balance can be calculated for each year and trends can be summarised by looking at readings over a period of time, usually a decade. From these longer-term trends the **cumulative net balance** can be calculated.

The Bench Mark Research Project carried out by the United States Geological Survey (USGS) measures longer term changes in the mass balance of four benchmark glaciers: Gulkana and Wolverine in Alaska, South Cascade in Washington State and, most recently, Sperry in Montana (since 2005). These glaciers are called benchmark glaciers because the aim of the project is to measure each glacier's response to climate change by providing long-term records of both annual and cumulative mass balance trends. Both the fieldwork methodology and analyses use common strategies to enable comparisons to be made between the glaciers, which were chosen as a representative sample of glaciers from across the USA (see Figure 4).

It is these longer-term trends that determine the 'health' of the glacier, and whether it will significantly advance or retreat. Currently it is estimated (largely using data from polar orbiting satellites) that 75% of the world's ice masses are experiencing 'rising trends' in their net negative balances, almost certainly as a result of short-term climate change (average global increase in surface temperature was 0.6°C in the last century, with rises of more than 2°C in the crucial areas of Greenland and the Antarctic Peninsula). The Arctic and east Antarctica ice sheets are thinning and melting, which has led to increasing concerns over the impact of global rises in sea levels.

Knowledge check 3

Define cumulative net balance.

Exam tip

Become practised at calculating means and totals of mass balance measurements in tables. They will be a feature of your AS exam.

Positive and negative feedback in the glacier system

Feedback effects are those that can amplify *or* diminish changes, for example in glacial mass balances.

Positive feedback can amplify small changes in a glacier budget in a variety of ways, such as:

1. **Snow and ice cover**. Small increases in show/ice cover raise the surface albedo (reflectivity) so more solar energy is reflected back into space — leading to further cooling, which could lead to further snowfall, and therefore to further ice cover.
2. **Melting of snow/ice cover** by climate warming from greenhouse gases (e.g. emissions of CO_2) decreases albedo, and methane is emitted as permafrost melts. The seas warm up, which causes calving of ice sheets, leading to even more losses of snow/ice cover and surface albedo, so decreasing reflectivity and accelerating further warming and yet further ice loss.

Negative feedback decreases the warming or cooling rates, which of course has an impact on ice cover. Increases in global warming will lead to more evaporation, and therefore more cloud cover. This is further enhanced by industrial pollution. Increasingly cloudy skies reflect more solar energy back into space, so diminishing global warming. Less intense global warming means the thinning of glaciers should decelerate and ultimately decrease.

Ice sheet dynamics can themselves disrupt the **thermohaline circulation**. Warming water in the Arctic disrupts the **Arctic conveyor** and this means less warm water from the Gulf Stream is drawn north to northwest Europe. This onset of colder conditions could lead to global cooling, with less ice melt, possibly an advance in glacier snouts and also diminishing numbers of icebergs calving into the ocean.

Feedback mechanisms are important in sustaining the trend towards warmer or colder conditions. These result in glacial and interglacial periods, as well as shorter-term stadials and interstadials such as the **Medieval Warm Period** and the **Little Ice Age**, both of which occurred in historic times and the impacts of which are well documented.

Knowledge check 4

Explain what is meant by the 'thermohaline circulation'.

Exam tip

Feedback is one of the key concepts within systems geography. Make sure you really understand it.

Summary

- The glacial system includes inputs, outputs, stores and transfers of energy and materials.
- Mass balance is the gains and losses of the ice store in the glacier system.
- Changes occur to the inputs to and outputs from a glacier over short- (annual) and long-term timescales. Longer term, the cumulative mass balance shows significant advance or retreat.
- The equilibrium point is reached when losses from ablation are balanced by gains from accumulation.
- The glacial budget is the annual growth and retreat of the glacier resulting from accumulation and ablation. A positive regime causes a glacier to grow, whereas a negative regime causes it to retreat.
- Positive feedback in the glacier system amplifies changes, for example in glacier mass balance, whereas negative feedback decreases changes.

Climate change and the glacier budget over different timescales

Causes of climate change through the Quaternary Ice Age

Many scientists say that we are currently living in the most recent Ice Age, the **Quaternary**, which began around 2 million years ago with the onset of global cooling and **ice-house** conditions following the end of the Tertiary period. Recent theories suggest that plate tectonics created suitable conditions to 'kick start' the Ice Age by positioning Antarctica as an isolated continent at the South Pole.

The Quaternary period is divided into two epochs of geological time, although many researchers argue that a third epoch should be added, called the **Anthropocene**, which is completely dominated by the impact of humans and their activities.

1 The **Pleistocene** covers the timespan from the beginning of the Quaternary to about 11,500 years ago when the most recent continental glacial ended.
2 The **Holocene** interglacial (the period in which we now live) is similar climatically to previous interglacials, but is distinctive for the beginning and growth of human civilisation, in particular agriculture and industrialisation.

Figure 3 summarises the characteristics of the Pleistocene — on a geological timescale it can be regarded as a single ice age, but as the figure shows there were multiple periods of glacials (colder **ice-house** conditions) and interglacials (**greenhouse** or warmer conditions).

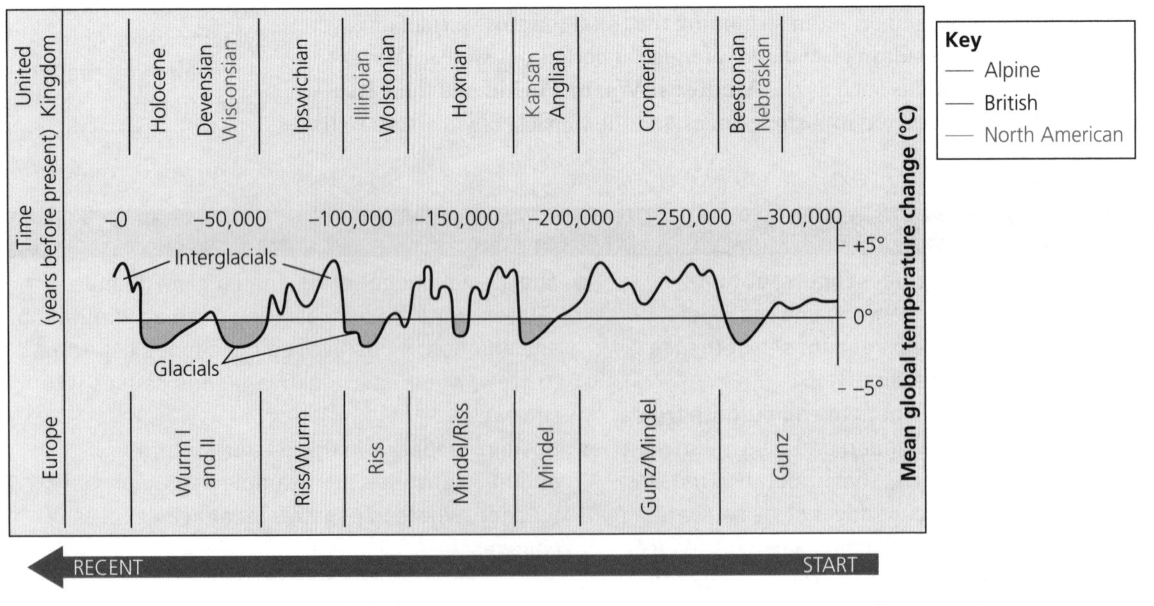

Figure 3 Ice age chronology

Figure 3 also shows numerous fluctuations within the major glacial/interglacial cycles, operating at a number of timescales. These shorter periods of intense cold are called **stadial** periods, with shorter periods of relative warmth, known as **interstadials**. Recent data from ice core sampling suggest that some of the more severe fluctuations in temperature actually occurred quite abruptly.

Causes of longer-term glacial/interglacial cycles

Long-term changes in the Earth's orbit around the sun are currently seen as the primary cause of the oscillations between glacial and interglacial conditions. The **Milankovitch theory**, based on **orbital/astronomic forcing** of glacial periods, takes into account three main characteristics of the Earth's orbit:

1. **Eccentricity** of the orbit: it changes from being more elliptical to more circular and back again over a period of around 100,000 years, thereby changing the amount of radiation received from the sun (this is considered to be the dominant factor).
2. **Axis tilt** varies from 21.8° to 24.4° (currently the tilt is 23.5°) over a timescale of around 41,000 years. This changes the sunshine intensity at the poles and therefore the seasonality of the Earth's climate. The greater the tilt, the greater the difference between summer and winter.
3. The Earth '**wobbles**' on its axis (just like a spinning top), changing the point in the year at which Earth is closest to the sun (**axial precession**), over a 21,000 year cycle. This causes long-term changes to when different seasons occur along the Earth's orbital path.

Exam tip

Explaining longer-term climate cycles is complex. Learn the facts thoroughly and accurately assess the evidence. Causality is complex.

The three orbital cycles can combine together to minimise the amount of solar energy reaching the northern hemisphere during summer (leading to cooler summers overall).

Milankovitch's theory is supported by the fact that glacials seem to have occurred at regular intervals of approximately 100,000 years. However, the actual impact of the combined orbital changes on solar radiation amount and distribution is small — probably only enough to change global temperatures by between 0.5°C and 1°C.

To explain the larger temperature changes of up to 5°C that were required for the vast expanses of ice to form, or to melt, we have to look at climate **feedback mechanisms**.

In conclusion, many scientists view Milankovitch cycles as a possible trigger to major ice-house–greenhouse changes or even as a good 'pacemaker' during each cycle, but climate feedback mechanisms are needed to sustain the drive towards either colder or warmer conditions that caused the glacial and interglacial periods (see p. 9).

Possible explanations for shorter-term fluctuations

As can be seen in Figure 3, both glacial and interglacial periods have fluctuations within them, with frequent warming (interstadials) and cooling (stadials) periods. As well as the combinations of effects in the Milankovich cycles, a number of factors have been cited for these shorter-term fluctuations.

Solar forcing

The amount of energy emitted by the sun varies depending on the number and density of sunspots (dark spots on the sun's surface caused by intense magnetic storms). There are a number of cycles of sunspot activity that vary in length, including 'the 11-year sunspot cycle'. There are reliable records of sunspot activity for the last 400 years, with some information for the last 2000 years. A longer period with no sunspot activity, known as the Maunder Minimum, occurred between 1645 and 1715, at the height of the Little Ice Age — to which it has often been linked. The preceding Medieval Warm Period has been linked to more intense sunspot activity. The difficulty with this explanation is that total variation in solar radiation caused by sunspot activity is only 0.1% and is not, by itself, enough to explain the climate fluctuations. Even so, some scientists suggest that around 20% of twentieth-century warming may be attributed to solar output variation.

Volcanic causes

Violent volcanic activity can alter global climate. Eruptions with a high VEI (volcanic explosivity index) of >4 eject huge volumes of ash, sulphur dioxide, water vapour and CO_2 into the atmosphere (volcanic aerosols) which are distributed around the globe by high-level winds. In 1815, Tambora in Indonesia ejected 200 million tonnes of SO_2 into the atmosphere, and in the following 2–3 years recorded temperatures were 0.4–0.7°C lower, resulting in short-lived global cooling.

Changes in the glacier budget through historical times: the Little Ice Age

The Little Ice Age was the longest glacial oscillation in historical times. The Little Ice Age was preceded by the Medieval Warm Period in the mid-fourteenth century. Over much of the globe most of the period between AD 1350 and 1900 was slightly colder, perhaps on average between 1.0°C and 2.0°C, than at present. However, between AD 1550 and 1750 there was a period of very cold conditions — the Little Ice Age — which occurred globally.

Knowledge check 5

Explain, using examples, what is meant by a 'proxy record'.

Proxy records from historical documents and paintings add detail to our knowledge of past climate and its impacts, including:

- the widespread abandonment of upland farms in Scandinavia and Iceland
- many glaciers in Europe readvanced down-valley, as the Little Ice Age was a period of predominantly positive net mass balance. These advances left prominent terminal moraines when the glaciers subsequently retreated, but this often occurred at different dates/times around the world
- Arctic sea ice spread further south, with polar bears frequently seen in Iceland
- rivers in the UK and lowland Europe, and New York harbour, froze over
- the national sport of curling developed in Scotland on the many frozen lakes and rivers

As with many medium-timescale stadials and interstadials, there is not one simple causal explanation. There is a definite link with sunspot activity — with periods of intense sunspot activity coinciding with warmer periods, and the Maunder Minimum (no sunspot activity, see above) with the coldest period in the Little Ice Age.

Some glaciologists see the Little Ice Age as the beginning of a new stadial and argue that it was the CO_2 emissions and sooty fumes from the onset of the Industrial Revolution that triggered recent warming, halting the Little Ice Age.

However, many scientists believe feedback loops are the key influence in the triggering of the stadial. Changes to the thermohaline circulation seem to be a probable factor — the diversion or blockage of the North Atlantic warming system made areas in the northern hemisphere much colder and therefore subject to glacier advance. The problem with this explanation is that the Little Ice Age was a worldwide event.

Seasonal cycles and their impact on the glacial budget

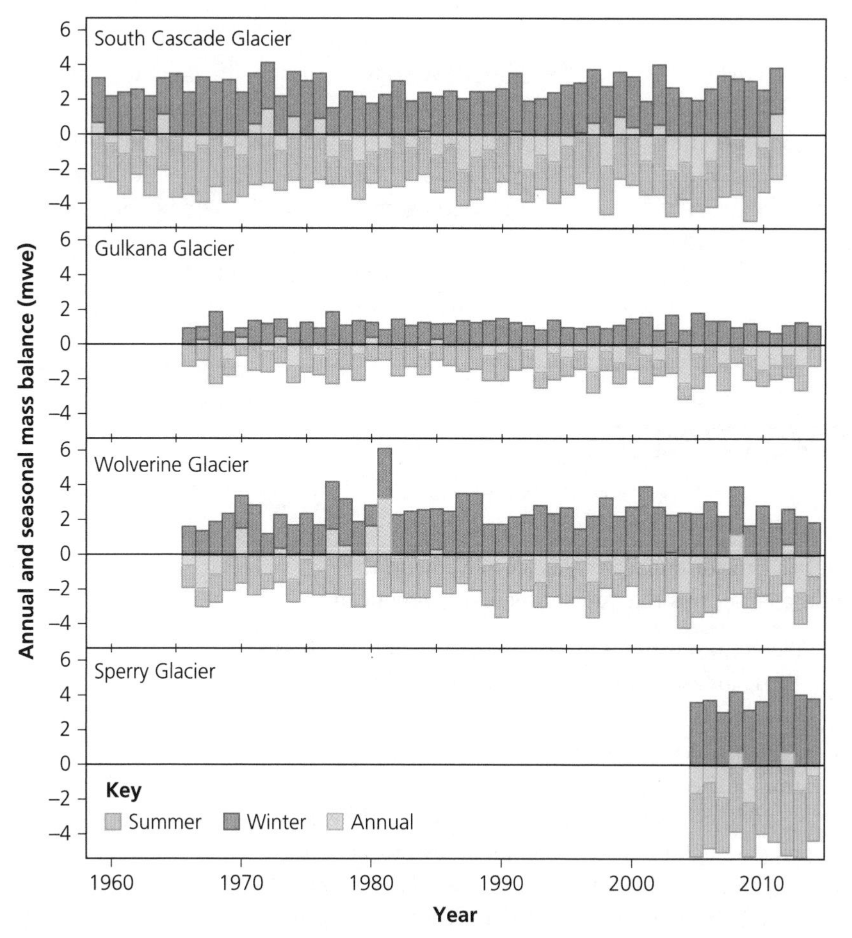

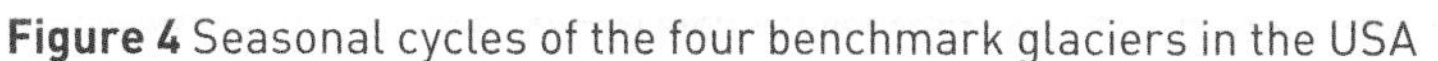
Figure 4 Seasonal cycles of the four benchmark glaciers in the USA

Figure 4 shows how the four benchmark glaciers vary, particularly in the range of their seasonal cycles.

Virtually all glaciers have a positive mass balance in winter, when accumulation exceeds ablation, and a negative mass balance in summer. The magnitude varies, both spatially and temporally, and this will affect the net balance overall, i.e. the difference between summer and winter measurements.

Exam tip

Cumulative balance is the overall impact of the totals of annual balances, which are largely negative.

Knowledge check 6

What are benchmark glaciers?

The prime reason for this is temperature — lower temperatures in winter can generate increased snow accumulation. Conversely, summer conditions with rising temperatures result in considerable ablation, with evaporation from the glacier surface, and meltwater losses. It only takes a series of hard winters or heatwave summers to cause significant variations in annual net balances.

This is the simplified picture but there are many other variables that make the issue more complex, such as the amount of debris that covers the glacier, the height of the glacier, the latitude of the glacier, or the degree of climate warming.

Summary

- Long-term changes are called glacials and interglacials, while short-term fluctuations are called stadials and interstadials.
- Long-term changes in the Earth's orbit around the sun (according to Milankovitch theory — eccentricity, axis tilt and wobble) may cause or trigger major changes, but climate feedback mechanisms are probably needed to sustain the drive towards colder or warmer conditions causing the glacial and interglacial periods.
- Other causal factors of short-term fluctuations include solar forcing, volcanic eruptions and their associated feedback mechanisms.
- Causes of changes in the glacial budget through historical time, such as the globally occurring Little Ice Age (AD 1550–1750), are complex but may include sunspot activity, the Industrial Revolution, changes to the thermohaline circulation, as well as feedback mechanisms.
- Seasonal changes are mainly the result of temperature which causes accumulation in winter and ablation in summer.

Glacier movement

Glacier regimes

The **thermal regime** of a glacier has a major impact on glacier movement, the operation of glacial processes and the landforms that are subsequently produced.

Glaciers have traditionally been divided into warm-based (temperate) glaciers, such as those found in the Alpine and sub-Arctic areas, known as wet glaciers, and cold-based (polar) glaciers.

- **Cold-based glaciers** occur in high latitudes, particularly in Antarctica and Greenland. The average temperature of the ice is usually well below 0°C as a result of surface temperatures as low as –20°C to –30°C, so the accumulation of heat from geothermal sources is not great enough to raise the temperature at the base of the glacier to 0°C, as the ice may be up to 500 m thick. There is relatively little surface melt in the very short and cool polar summer, so little meltwater percolates downwards. The glacier is permanently frozen to its bed, so there is no debris-rich basal layer.
- Outside the polar region, for example in high-altitude areas, most glaciers are the **warm-based** temperate type. The temperature of the surface layer fluctuates above and below melting point, depending on the time of year, whereas the temperature of the rest of the ice, extending downwards to the base, is close to melting point. Because of increased pressure of overlying ice, water exists as a liquid at temperatures below 0°C, causing the basal ice to melt continuously. The

Knowledge check 7

Summarise the differences between temperate and polar glaciers (use Figure 5).

effects of pressure, geothermal energy and percolation of meltwater all contribute to prevent the glacier freezing to its bed. The glacier has lots of debris in its basal layers, and significant subglacial depositional features. Figure 5 summarises the contrasting temperature profiles of the two types of glacier and the key temperature controls within a glacier.

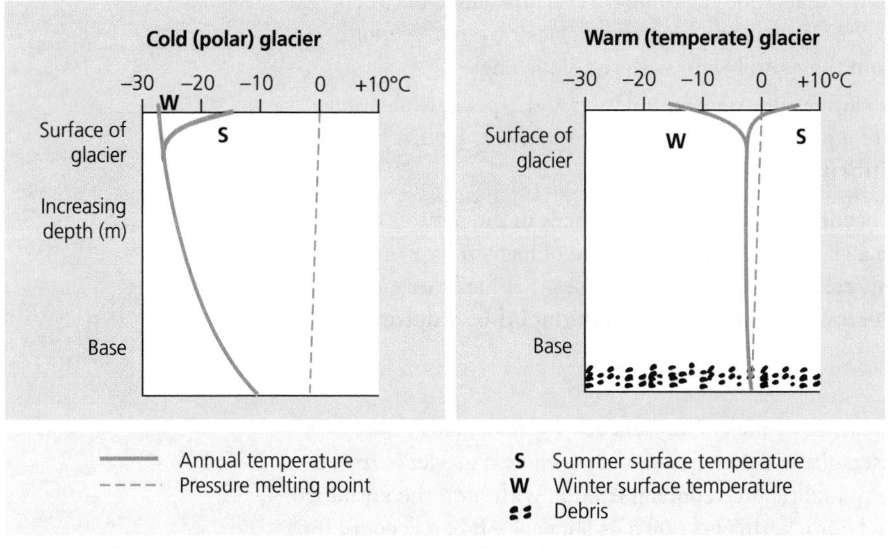

Figure 5 The contrasting temperature profiles of temperate and polar glaciers

A third subdivision of the regime classification is the hybrid **polythermal** glacier. This is where the underneath of the main glacier is warm- (wet) based and its margin cold-based. Many large glaciers are cold-based in their upper regions and warm-based lower down, when they extend into warmer climate zones — this is a common occurrence in Svalbard. The basal thermal regime can vary more locally according to ice thickness, shape of underlying bed, gradient and also differences in the amount of pressure near the base. Polythermal glaciers frequently have thick debris-rich basal ice layers in their lower areas, often with many meltwater channels at their margin and underneath, producing hummocky moraines.

Surging glaciers or **ice streams** may occur within warm-based, cold-based or polythermal glaciers, and may have rates of flow up to 100 m per day (e.g. the Greenland outlet glaciers which average 30 m per day) with huge amounts of **calving** (see p. 18).

Glacier movement

The fundamental cause of ice movement is gravity. Ice moves downslope from higher altitudes to lower areas either on land or at sea level. As the ice mass builds up over time in the accumulation zone, the weight of the snow and ice exerts an increasing downslope force due to gravity (known as **shear stress**). Shear stress increases as the slope angle increases and, once the shear stress is great enough to overcome the resisting forces of ice strength and friction, the glacier ice pulls away and moves downward away from the zone of accumulation. The momentum of the ice movement downwards towards the ablation zone prevents further build-up, thereby maintaining the glacier at a state of **dynamic equilibrium** with the slope angle. This forward movement of glacial ice towards the margins/snout occurs regardless of whether the glacier as a whole is advancing or retreating. Therefore the speed of glacier movement forward depends on the degree of imbalance in, or the gradient between, the zone of accumulation and the zone of ablation.

- **Warm**, **wet-based** glaciers in temperate maritime climates experience greater snowfall in winter and more rapid ablation in summer. The imbalance between accumulation and ablation zones is therefore greater, so glacier ice moves more rapidly downslope to maintain the equilibrium with the slope angle.
- In **cold-based** glaciers, the slower rates of accumulation and especially ablation result in a smaller gradient of equilibrium and slow ice movement. Figure 1 on p. 7 demonstrates **glacier equilibrium**.

Other variations in movement occur because of the differences in the nature of the **substrate** (base) on which a glacier rests and the nature of its own base, as this determines the relative importance of the three processes that facilitate glacier movement: **basal sliding**, **internal deformation** and **subglacial bed deformation**.

Basal sliding

Basal sliding relates to the presence of meltwater beneath a glacier. This type of ice movement applies to warm-based glaciers and cannot occur where a glacier is frozen to its bed. The meltwater acts as a lubricant, reducing friction with both the entrained debris and with the underlying bedrock (this is known as slippage). It can account for up to 75% of glacier movement in warm-based glaciers.

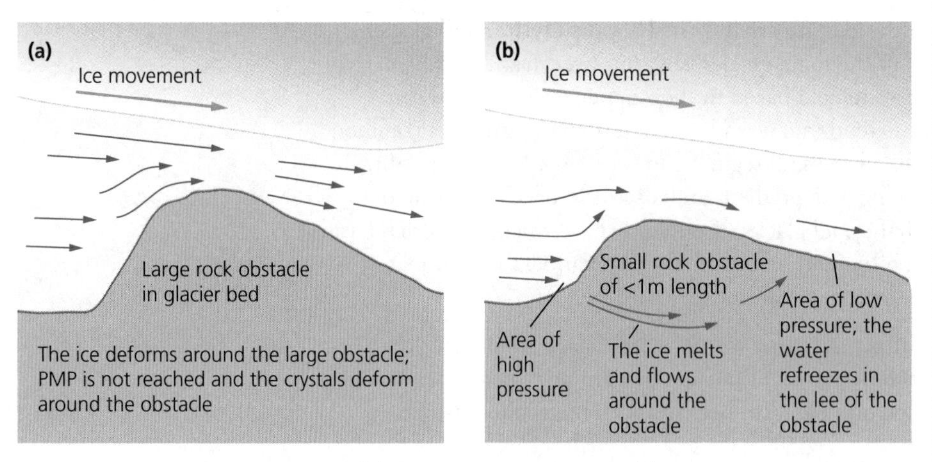

Figure 6 Basal sliding. (a) Enhanced basal creep, (b) regelation slip

Two specific processes enable glaciers to slide over their beds (Figure 6):

1. **Enhanced basal creep**, whereby basal ice deforms around irregularities on the underlying bedrock surface.
2. **Regelation slip**, which occurs as basal ice deforms under pressure when encountering obstructions such as 'rock steps'. As the glacier moves over the obstruction, the pressure on the basal ice increases up-glacier, causing it to reform in a plastic state as a result of melting under this pressure. Once the glacier has flowed over the obstruction the pressure is lowered and the meltwater refreezes.

Internal deformation

Cold-based polar glaciers are unable to move by basal sliding as their basal temperature is below the pressure melting point. Instead, they move by internal deformation, which has two main elements:

1. Intergranular flow, when individual ice crystals deform and move in relation to each other.
2. Laminar flow, where there is movement of individual layers within the glacier.

The deformation of ice in response to stress is known as **ice creep** and is a result of the increased ice thickness and/or the surface slope angle. In some cases where ice creep cannot respond quickly enough to the stress, **ice faulting** occurs, creating a variety of crevasse types at the surface.

When the slope gradient is increased, there is acceleration of ice movement and **extensional flow**. This can occur in the zone of accumulation and can result in an **ice fall**. With many crevasses near the ablation zone, where there is usually a reduction of slope angle, the ice decelerates and there is **compressional flow**, which creates a series of thrust faults in the ice, with closed up crevasses.

Knowledge check 8

Summarise the impact of glacier temperature regime on glacier movement.

Subglacial bed deformation

Subglacial bed deformation occurs locally when a glacier moves over relatively weak or unconsolidated rock, and the sediment itself can deform under the weight of the glacier, moving the ice 'on top' of it along with it. Locally this process can often account for up to 90% of the forward motion of glacier ice in polythermal outlet glaciers, such as in Iceland.

The velocity of glacier ice

The overall velocity of the glacier results from a combination of the processes described above.

Warm-based glaciers have a greater overall velocity of ice movement than cold-based glaciers because they are also subject to basal sliding, as well as the internal deformation and flow that affects both types. Even greater velocities are reached when a warm-based glacier moves over deformable sediment.

Observations of glaciers across the world have shown great variations in the total velocity of glacier ice, with most glaciers having velocities of between 3 m and 300 m per year.

A number of factors have an impact on the rate of movement:

- altitude, which affects the temperatures and precipitation inputs
- slope, which can be directly related to flow — steeper slopes lead to faster speeds
- lithology, which can affect basal processes and the possibility of subglacial bed deformation
- size, which can affect the rapidity of response
- mass balance, which affects the equilibrium of the glacier and also whether it is advancing or retreating

Glacial surges

Glacial surges are a common feature of glaciers in Alaska. Surges are periods of rapid movement when a glacier snout advances up to 1000 times faster than normal as a result of a change in the flow pattern of subglacial meltwater.

- Water builds up underneath the glaciers during a phase of normal glacier flow and there is an increase and thickening of ice in the accumulation zone.
- During winter, subglacial meltwater channels are closed — increasing ice accumulation.
- During summer, the weight of ice accumulation is so great that still the subglacial channels do not open.
- Pressure melting point and the subglacial water separates the basal ice from its bed, so lubricating it and causing the overlying ice to flow more readily.
- Abundant water increases the pore water pressure of the subglacial sediment, which adds to the rapid movement.
- The surge occurs and the glacier resumes normal flow — this cycle occurs as frequently as every 10–20 years.

Glaciologists have carried out research into glacier velocities around the world. To measure velocity at the surface of the glacier they drive a series of stakes into the surface and survey the position of the stakes annually. It is more difficult to measure the rates of glacier movement at depths below the surface. Perutz developed a series of flexible poles to do this and noted that movement was fastest just below the surface. In either case, the effect of friction of the glacier bottom and valley sides can be seen.

Summary

- Cold-based glaciers occur in high latitudes and move slowly, by internal deformation, whereas warm-based glaciers occur in temperate regions and move rapidly, by basal sliding.
- The primary cause of ice movement is gravity, with rates of movement dependent on the degree of imbalance, or the gradient, between the zone of accumulation and the zone of ablation.
- Glacial movements include internal deformation, basal sliding, subglacial bed deformation, surges and compressional/extensional flow.

The range of glacial environments and their distribution

The **cryosphere** is the parts of the Earth's crust and atmosphere that are below 0°C for at least part of each year. It consists of ice sheets and glaciers, together with sea ice, lake ice, ground ice (permafrost) and snow cover. Mass and energy are constantly exchanged between the cryosphere and other major components of Earth systems: the hydrosphere, lithosphere, atmosphere and biosphere. Glaciers are visible and sensitive barometers of climate change because they constantly grow/advance and shrink/retreat in response to changes in temperature and precipitation.

Exam tip

You need to understand the variety of glacial landscapes that occur.

Types of ice mass and glacial environments

Table 1 shows how ice masses can be classified by their morphological characteristics, size and location.

Table 1 Different types of ice mass

Type of ice mass	Description	Size in km²	Degree of constraint*	Example
Ice sheet	Complete submergence of regional topography, forms a gently sloping dome of ice several kilometres thick in the centre	100,000–10 million	U	Greenland and Antarctica
Ice cap	Occupies upland areas, a smaller version of an ice sheet. Outlet glaciers and ice sheets drain both ice sheets and ice caps	3–10,000	U	Vatnajokull (Iceland)
Ice field	Ice covering an upland area but not thick enough to bury topography. Many do not extend beyond highland source	10–10,000	U	Patagonia (Chile), Columbia (Canada)
Valley glacier	Glacier confined between valley walls and terminating in a narrow tongue. Forms from ice caps/sheets or cirques. May terminate in sea as a tidewater glacier	3–1500	C	Aletsch Glacier (Switzerland), Athabasca (Canada)
Piedmont glacier	Valley glacier that extends beyond the end of a mountain valley into a flatter area and spreads out as a fan	3–1000	C	Malaspina (Alaska)
Cirque glacier	Smaller glacier occupying a hollow on the mountain side — it carves out a corrie or cirque; a smaller version is known as a niche glacier	0.5–8	C	Hodges Glacier (South Georgia)
Ice shelf, sometimes known as sea ice	Large area of floating glacier ice extending from the coast where several glaciers have reached the sea and coalesce	10–100,000	U	Ronne and Ross Ice Shelf (Antarctica)

*C (constrained), U (unconstrained)

Present and past distributions of ice cover

At **present**, glaciers cover more than 10% of the Earth's land area, and 75% of the world's fresh water is locked up in this ice cover (ice sheets and valley glaciers) — about 1.8% of all the water (fresh, brackish or salt) on Earth.

Table 2 compares the distribution of present-day and late Pleistocene ice sheets and glaciers in both the northern and southern hemispheres, and shows that:

- about 85% of all current glacier ice is contained in Antarctica (shared between West and East Antarctic Ice Sheets)
- the Greenland Ice Sheet is the second largest accumulation of glacier ice, holding nearly 11% of Earth's total ice cover
- the remaining ice cover is distributed amongst ice caps such as Vatnajokull (Iceland) and north Canada and Alaska, highland ice fields (Colombia) and many smaller glaciers in high-altitude areas (Himalayas, Rockies, Cascades, Andes, European Alps etc.)
- there are even glaciers above 4000 m in Ecuador in the High Andes, Mount Kilimanjaro in Tanzania and in Indonesia, in Equatorial regions

Table 2 Estimates of ice cover, present and past

Region	Present estimated area (10^6 km^2)	Past (late Pleistocene–Quaternary Ice Age)
Antarctica	13.50	14.50
Greenland	1.80	2.35
Arctic basin	0.24	
Alaska	0.05	16.00
Rest of North America	0.03	
Andes	0.03	0.88
European Alps	0.004	0.04
Scandinavia	0.004	6.60
Asia	0.12	3.90
Africa	0.0001	0.0003
Australasia	0.001	0.7
Britain	0.0	0.34
Total	15.8	44.68

A number of factors influence the distribution of ice cover. Today the two most important factors are **latitude** (for polar ice masses) and **altitude** (for alpine glaciers). In high latitudes, the sun's rays hit the ground at a lower angle and the solar energy received has to heat a larger area, whereas at high altitudes there is the impact of the **environmental lapse rate** (ELR) whereby temperature reduces by 1°C for every 100 m of altitude. Other factors are also locally significant, such as **aspect** which can determine the amount of snow that falls and settles. In mountain areas, aspect and relief combine to affect the distribution of cirque glaciers. In the northern hemisphere north- and east-facing slopes are both more sheltered and more shaded and thus more likely to experience snow accumulation (see p. 24).

Table 2 shows the following differences:

- Ice cover was about three times greater than present at the Pleistocene maximum.
- Antarctica and Greenland ice sheets covered a slightly greater area than they do today.
- The major extensions were to ice sheets in North America (Laurentide and Cordilleran) and the Scandinavian ice sheet in Europe — these all grew to thicknesses of 3000 to 4000 m and transformed the landscape of North America and Europe, respectively.
- Other significant extensions included all of southern South America, South Island New Zealand, west and east Siberia, and the Himalayas, where ice caps fed numerous valley glaciers.

Summary

- The **cryosphere** consists of ice sheets, glaciers (valley, piedmont and cirques), sea ice, lake ice, ground ice (permafrost) and snow cover. All these, except permafrost and snow cover, are ice masses.
- During the Quaternary Ice Age, at its maximum ice cover was three times greater than today, with major ice sheets in North America, Scandinavia, southern South America, South Island New Zealand, west and east Siberia, and the Himalayas.
- Today, about 85% of glacier ice is in Antarctica, with 11% in the Greenland Ice Sheet and the rest distributed amongst ice caps and many smaller glaciers in high-altitude areas, but with a few glaciers at very high altitudes in Equatorial regions.

Processes of glacial weathering and erosion

The glacier landform system

The movement of the ice allows the ice sheet or glacier (ice mass) to pick up debris and erode at its base and sides, as well as to transport and modify the materials it is carrying. The more rapid this movement is, the more likely the glacier is to transform the landscape. Conversely, stagnant ice, a frequent 'state' of lowland ice sheets, is more likely to 'protect the landscape' and only reshape it by dumping huge amounts of debris.

A combination of both direct ice action and indirect impact, such as the formation of fluvioglacial features by meltwater, disturbance of pre-existing drainage systems and complex ice-induced sea level changes, shapes glacial landscapes.

Inputs	→	Throughput	→	Outputs	→	Landscapes
Controlling factors e.g. climate, ice thickness		Processes of erosion, transport and deposition		Landforms at macro, meso and micro scales		Products of assemblages of landforms

Figure 7 How the glacier landform system works

Sources of glacial debris

In order to erode, a glacier or ice mass needs tools. **Freeze–thaw weathering** (frost shattering) is caused by the physical force of water freezing in cracks and joints in the rock and then expanding by up to 9%, so wedging rocks apart to form angular debris (scree). For freeze–thaw processes to operate effectively there needs to be frequent temperature fluctuations around freezing point (an active freeze–thaw cycle). The angular debris falls down the side of the mountain to join other **supraglacial sources** of material, which include that being washed or blown on to the glacier from the surrounding land, plus atmospheric fallout such as volcanic ash (common in Iceland).

How much debris is produced depends on the geology (the character of the jointing and bedding in the rocks), the amount of water present, and the frequency and range of temperature fluctuations. Therefore, freeze–thaw is especially important in cirque and valley glaciers as these have an adjoining marginal mountain area that is not covered by ice and so provides abundant debris from rock falls and debris flows. This is in contrast to ice sheets where subglacial processes are more significant.

Subglacial sources include material eroded from the glacier bed and valley walls, material frozen to the base of the glacier from subglacial streams, as well as **englacial** material that has worked its way down through the glacier or ice sheet.

Glacial erosion is the removal of material by ice and meltwater and involves a combination of several processes:

- **Abrasion** by individual clasts, which results in micro features such as striations and chatter marks. Additionally, rock flour (grade sizes under 0.1 mm in diameter) polishes the underlying rocks by a 'sand paper' action.

- **Plucking** is often referred to as **glacial quarrying**. Quarrying is a two-stage process, with the joints initially widened by fracture and subsequent entrainment of any loosened material. The importance of plucking is dependent on rock type and the existence of pre-existing joints.
- **Fracture** and **traction** occur as a result of the **crushing** effect of the weight of moving ice passing over the rock, and variations in pressures lead to freezing and thawing of the meltwater (**basal melting**) which aids the plucking process (see p. 30).
- **Dilation** occurs as overlying material is moved, causing fractures in the rock parallel to erosion surfaces as the bedrock adjusts to the unloading.
- **Subglacial meltwater erosion** can be both mechanical (similar to fluvial erosion except that the water is under hydrostatic pressure) and chemical, whereby glacial meltwater can dissolve minerals and carry away the solutes, especially in limestone rocks.

Factors affecting glacial erosion

There is great variation in the intensity of glacial erosion. The most important single factor that determines the efficiency of glacial erosion is the glacier itself — its size, which determines ice thickness, and its thermal regime, which determines the importance and intensity of the erosional processes. All types of glacial erosion operate more effectively when glacier ice is warm-based — meltwater and abundant debris facilitate abrasion, and **regelation** (one of the key elements of the plucking process) can also occur.

Other important factors influencing the rate of glacier erosion include the glacier velocity across the bed, which, combined with ice thickness, affects the power of the glacier to cause shattering. The quantity and shape of the rock debris (subaerial processes of freeze–thaw or **congelifraction**), combined with extensive mass movement from scree slopes to supply the tools for glacial erosion, are also important. Characteristics of the bedrock, such as density of jointing and hardness, are also significant in influencing compressional and extensional flow (see p. 17).

Essentially, erosion rates are more intense when glaciers are warm-based, thick and fast-moving, and the bedrock relatively weak, often because of dense jointing. Erosion rates are much slower where glaciers are cold-based and the rock relatively resistant.

Features and landforms of glacial erosion

As Figure 8 shows, landforms result from the interaction of the processes and characteristics of the landscape experiencing glaciations (bedrock type, structure and topography, shape and relief of land) operating through time. However, the processes do not operate at a constant rate and landforms continually adjust, especially after glacial retreat in the short **paraglacial** period, and then post-glacially when landforms originally shaped by glaciation are reshaped by water, weathering and mass movement.

A further complication is that most present-day landscapes resulting from glaciation are **polycyclic/genetic**, the product of many successive advances of glacier ice because of alternating ice-house–greenhouse conditions during the Quaternary period. As the last glacial (the Loch Lomond stadial) ended relatively recently (in terms of geological

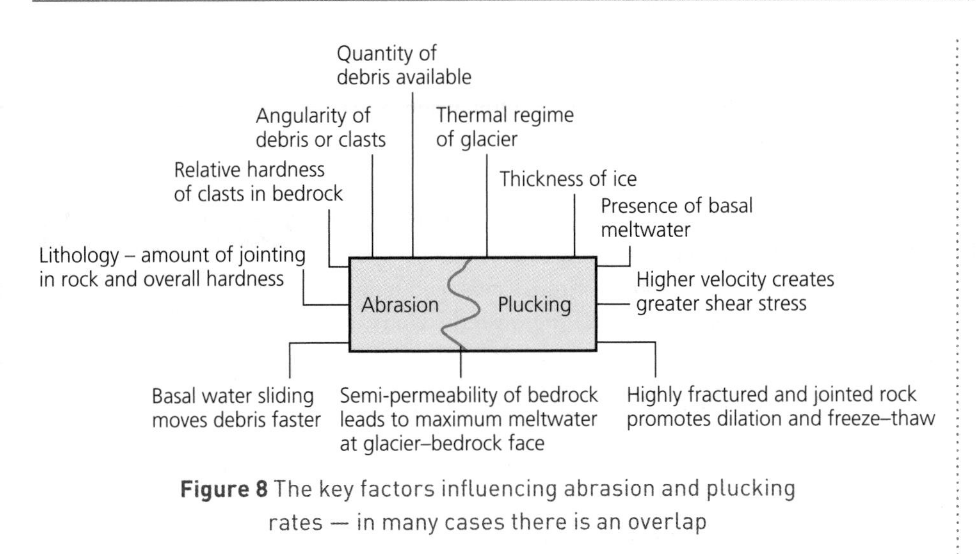

Figure 8 The key factors influencing abrasion and plucking rates — in many cases there is an overlap

time — around 11,500 years ago), the mountain areas of the UK (the Cairngorms and northwest Highlands of Scotland, the Lake District and North Wales) provide clear examples of glacial erosional landforms.

Table 3 provides a checklist of a range of landforms associated with glaciated highland erosion, classified by scale.

Table 3 Checklist of landforms associated with glaciated highland erosion

	Landform	Appearance	Formation
Macro	Cirque (or corrie)	An armchair-shaped hollow on a hillside above a glacial valley	A pre-glacial hollow is enlarged by plucking and abrasion as ice moves in a rotational manner under gravity
	Arête	A narrow ridge between two cirques	As two cirques are enlarged back to back the ridge between them becomes increasingly narrowed
	Pyramidal peak	A sharp, pointed hilltop	As three or more cirques are enlarged the hilltop between becomes increasingly sharp and pointed
	Trough (or U-shaped valley)	A steep-sided, flat-floored, straight valley	A pre-glacial river valley is widened and deepened by erosion from an advancing glacier
	Truncated spur	A steep and possibly rocky section of the side of a trough	The pre-glacial interlocking spurs of the river valley are eroded by the much more powerful glacier
	Hanging valley	A small tributary valley high above the floor of the trough, often with a waterfall	Tributary glaciers with small amounts of ice that did not erode their valley floor as deeply as the main glacier and so are left at a higher altitude
	Ribbon lake	A long deep lake on the floor of a glacial trough	The ice erodes and deepens parts of the floor of the glacial trough. A long lake forms, which may be dammed by a rock bar or a terminal moraine
Meso	Roche moutonnée	Asymmetrical, bare rock outcrop with a gently sloping side facing up-valley	As ice crosses a resistant rock outcrop, the increased pressure causes melting and basal sliding and the up-valley side is smoothed by abrasion. On the leeward side pressure is reduced, refreezing occurs and plucking takes place, causing a steep, jagged slope
	Crag and tail	Large ice-eroded crag with tapering tail on leeside	Formed by hard igneous rock protecting rocks from weathering and erosion
Micro	Striations	Grooves on exposed rocks	Abrasion by debris embedded in the base of the glacier as it passed over bare rock. They can indicate the direction of ice movement

Macro-scale features

Macro-scale features are around 1 km or greater in size. These are the major elements in a glaciated highland landscape and contain many of the meso- and micro-scale erosional features, as well as depositional landforms.

Cirques (corries, cwms) are armchair- or bowl-shaped depressions usually found at relatively high altitudes. The initial stage of formation is for snow to accumulate in a sheltered mountainside location. In the northern hemisphere, cirques most commonly form on the northeastern side of mountains, in the lee of prevailing westerly winds, and in the shadier sites protected from insolation.

Knowledge check 9

Explain why the northeast aspect is the most favourable for corrie development in the northern hemisphere.

Once a sheltered area has accumulated snow, **nivation** or snow patch erosion begins, enlarging the hollow by a combination of freeze–thaw weathering to loosen the rock and, in summer, meltwater from melting snow transporting the rock debris away, thus enlarging the hollow. Once a **nivation hollow** (a periglacial feature) is established, **positive feedback** occurs, as the enlarged hollow traps additional snow and the hollows gradually enlarge to provide a site for glacial ice formation.

The processes of plucking and abrasion combine to develop the cirque (see Figure 18, p. 46). The glacier ice may expand in area and move down-valley during a glacial period. The cirque can be modified post-glacially with the formation of a small lake known as a tarn (e.g. Red Tarn on the northeast face of Helvellyn in the Lake District).

The erosion of cirque headwalls backwards into the slopes behind can result in the formation of an **arête** (a steep knife-like ridge produced from the intersection of two cirque headwalls) on either side of a slope divide. If three or more cirques interact back to back around the flanks of a mountain a steep, pointed peak is produced called a **horn** (as in Matterhorn) or a pyramidal peak because of its shape.

Glacial troughs

When glacier ice moves through mountain valleys, it straightens, widens and deepens them, changing them from V-shaped to U-shaped. More accurately, these glacial troughs are described as **parabolic** in shape. Glacial troughs can vary in length, from around 5 km long (Nant Ffrancon in Snowdonia) to spectacular features such as Yosemite Valley in California (about 12 km long). Along their length (long profile) many glacial troughs have a stepped profile, reflecting differential erosion as a result of both irregularities in the underlying bedrock and variations in intensity of erosion. For example, where several cirque glaciers meet at the head of a valley the enlarged glacier erodes deeply to form a trough end to the valley. After deglaciation, successive rock basins down a glacial trough are separated by **riegels** or rock steps. Longer and deeper basins may contain linear lakes, termed ribbon or finger lakes, many of which are now beginning to infill (Interlaken in Switzerland is built on an alluvial flat which has divided an original large lake to form Lake Thun and Lake Brienz). Post-glacial weathering and mass movement has caused infill of glacial troughs which are now commonly occupied by misfit streams.

Exam tip

Learn an annotated diagram of a particular valley to include in your essays. They should be easy and quick to draw and should locate examples of all the long features.

With relative sea level rises at the end of the last glaciation, many coastal glacial troughs were flooded by the sea to form sea lochs (Scotland) or **fjords** in Norway.

Hanging valleys occur where a small side tributary glacier meets a larger main valley glacier. During the glacial phase the elevation of the surface ice of the tributary and main valley glaciers is the same, but because the rate of erosion beneath the main valley glacier is much greater, once the glaciers have retreated the tributary valley can be left hanging hundreds of metres above, often with a waterfall plunging from the hanging valley to the main valley below (for example, Pistyll Rhaeadr in the Berwyn Mountains).

Many glacial troughs have **truncated spurs**, marked by steep, almost vertical side walls, where original interlocking spurs have been cut away or truncated by glacial erosion because of the inflexibility of glaciers moving down the valley (e.g. Lauterbrunnen valley in Switzerland or Yosemite in California).

Meso-scale features

Meso-scale features are largely found within macro features, for example the **whale backs** and **roches moutonnées** found on the floor of the Yosemite glacial trough. These intermediate-scale landforms can range from around 10 m to 1 km in length. Streamlined bedrock features such as whale backs are the most common, caused where a glacier moves over a resistant rock knoll, so abrading it.

Roches moutonnées are stoss and lee features, as abrasion smooths the up-glacier **stoss** side of a bedrock knoll, while glacial plucking makes the down-glacier **lee** side ragged and rough, thus producing an asymmetric rocky landform that was formed beneath the ice.

Crag and tail landforms occur where glacier ice is forced to flow around a large and resistant rock obstacle such as a volcanic plug, e.g. Edinburgh Castle plug. The hard rock obstacle (crag) protects less resistant material on the leeside from erosion, causing the feature to taper in the down-glacier direction (tail). The result is a crag with a steep up-glacier **stoss** end, and a long gently sloping, tapering **leeside**. In Edinburgh the Royal Mile runs down the tail for 1.4 km to Holyrood Palace. On the stoss side, Edinburgh Castle rock is 110 m high. You can see the scratch marks made by intense erosion when the ice sheet encountered the crag. This process occurred repeatedly over many glacial phases.

Micro-scale features

Micro features of glacial erosion are a few metres or less in size. They include **striations**, which are scratches on hard bedrock caused by debris being dragged across the bedrock surface during abrasion — almost like chisel marks. They tend to be orientated parallel to the direction of ice movement, with the deepest part of the scratch at the initial point of impact, and they are therefore useful for tracking the direction of past glacier movement. **Chatter marks** are irregular chips and fractures in the rock, whereas **crescentic gouges** have a more regular pattern and are usually concave up-glacier.

Micro features are not only useful for helping glaciologists understand from which direction the ice came (**provenance**) but also for determining the maximum altitude of glacier ice erosion, for example during the Loch Lomond stadial readvance. There

Knowledge check 10

Explain how glacial erosional features can be used to show the provenance of ice.

are no micro features above the **trim line** on the valley side. In the Glyders, North Wales, you can see how block fields, screes and tors, clearly indicative of periglacial activity, supersede abraded ice-scratched rocks above the trimline.

Summary

- Freeze–thaw weathering (frost shattering) provides materials for erosion, from supraglacial, subglacial and englacial sources.
- Glacial erosion is the removal of material by ice and meltwater and involves a combination of abrasion, plucking, fracture and traction, dilation and subglacial meltwater erosion.
- Factors affecting glacial erosion include the basal thermal regime, ice velocity, ice thickness, bedrock permeability and jointing of the rock.
- Glacial landforms at the macro-scale include cirques, pyramidal peaks, arêtes, glacial troughs, ribbon lakes, hanging valleys and truncated spurs. At the meso-scale they include roche moutonnées, crag and tail; and at the micro-scale they include striations.

Processes of glacial and fluvioglacial transport and deposition

As a glacier moves it transports huge amounts of debris. Once the material is **entrained** (picked up; see Figure 9) the glacier acts like a 'conveyor belt', carrying the material in three main ways.

1. **Supraglacial transport** is where frost-shattered, avalanche and other debris falls on to the glacier from the valley side. The material is angular and unsorted as it has not yet undergone abrasion.
2. **Englacial transport** occurs as the ice moves differentially and forms crevasses (see p. 21). Slope debris falls into the crevasses and becomes trapped in the glacial ice, so moving within the glacier, sometimes by meltwater.
3. **Subglacial transport** occurs at the glacial base. The collection of basal load is complex. Small fragments can be entrained by **basal ice freezing** around the particles, then applying sufficient force to drag them along, or ice may envelop a large boulder by **deformation flow** and drag it along the glacier base by **traction**. Large quantities of basal debris are joined by some englacial material washed down by meltwater streams. Where the ice bed is irregular, the processes of **pressure melt** and **regelation** combine to abrade and pluck material from the bedrock.

The presence of large boulders, known as glacial **erratics** because they are of a different rock type to the bedrock they 'sit' on, testifies to the sheer scale of the ability of glaciers (especially vast ice sheets) to transport enormous quantities and weight of rock debris, often over great distances. For example, huge erratics, boulders weighing up to 16,000 tonnes, were carried more than 300 km from the Canadian Rockies to the plains of Alberta by the Cordilleran Ice Sheet. Some erratics are dumped as perched boulders, for example the Bowder Stone in Borrowdale in the Lake District. If the erratic is made of rock of a distinctive geology from a restricted location — for example, Ailsa Craig granite from western Scotland — it is possible to precisely map the direction of glacier movement. For example, on the Northumberland,

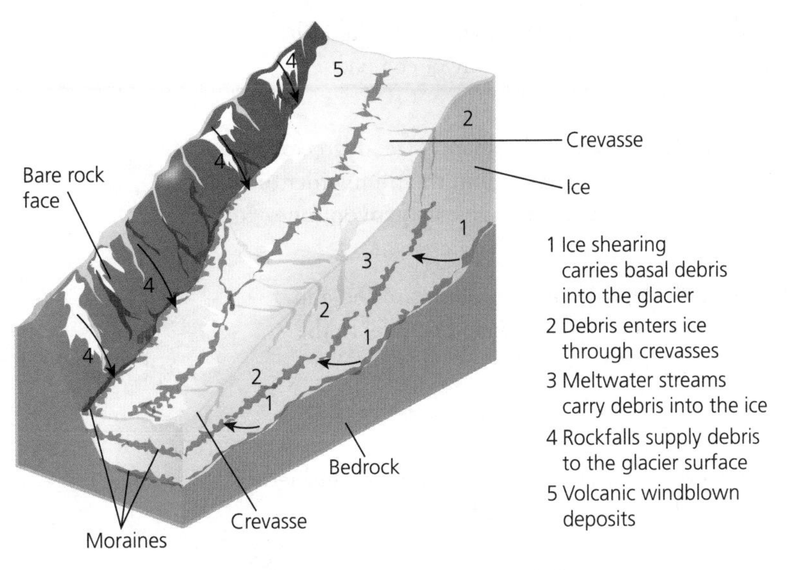

Figure 9 The glacier conveyor belt

Durham and Yorkshire coasts, erratics from Scandinavia have been found in the boulder clay, confirming the presence of Scandinavian continental ice sheets just offshore.

The processes of glacial deposition

The main processes by which glaciers deposit material are as follows.

- **Lodgement** occurs beneath the ice mass when subglacial debris that was being transported becomes 'lodged' or stuck on the glacier bed. Lodgement occurs when the friction between the subglacial debris and the bed becomes greater than the drag of the ice moving over it, so it is commonly associated with glaciers carrying huge loads of debris, and where the glacier is slow-moving or static.
- **Ablation** is the dumping of debris as the glacier melts and thaws. It can include supra- and englacial material as well as subglacial material.
- **Deformation** is less common and is associated with weak underlying bedrock — these sediments are deformed by the movement of the glacier.
- **Flow** occurs if high meltwater content causes the glacial debris to creep, slide or flow during deposition.

These processes produce **till** or boulder clay of different compositions, allowing scientists to analyse the types of depositional process.

- **Lodgement till** has relatively rounded clasts, because of the grinding that occurs at the ice bed interface, not within a matrix of clay or silt size particles (rock flour). It forms till sheets, as well as drumlins (see p. 28).
- **Ablation till** consists of more angular clasts, as they are not ground down, and also the matrix is of larger size material, less compact and largely unsorted. It is dumped by melting of slow-moving or stagnant ice and forms hummocks of moraine, often found at glacial margins.
- **Modified** or **deformation till** is reworked older deposits, with a variety of folds and faults indicating deformation by a moving glacier. It can form low ridges

transverse to the ice direction or, when it is formed by the flow of saturated till slurry during the summer season, can form thin sheets, usually of compact clay showing some layering.

Till **fabric analysis** is a technique that is used to look at the shape, size, degree of stratification of layering, and sorting (grading) of the clasts within the till in order to determine its origin, mode of formation and, if it contains erratics, its **provenance** (i.e. which direction the ice came from).

In general, glacial, as opposed to fluvioglacial, deposits are angular, unsorted and unstratified, although the long axes of the **clasts** are often aligned parallel to the direction of ice flow.

Landforms of glacial deposition

Moraine is an accumulation of glacial debris, whether dumped by an active glacier or left behind as a deposit after glacial retreat. There are two broad categories:

1 subglacial: formed beneath the glacier
2 ice-marginal: formed along the margins of a glacier

Subglacially formed moraines

These moraines are composed primarily of lodgement till as they are formed from debris beneath the glacier. **Till plains** of ground moraine are extensive flat areas that cover pre-existing topography, often to depths of 50 m. In some places beneath active glaciers, lodgement till is moulded into streamlined mounds, called **drumlins**, that have their long axis orientated parallel to the direction of ice movement.

Drumlins vary widely in size, usually ranging from 10 to 50 m high and between 200 and 2000 m long. The steeper, blunt end of the drumlin (stoss end) is the up-glacier side, whereas the gently sloping, tapered end occurs down-glacier. Drumlins usually occur in 'swarms', forming what is often called '**basket of eggs topography**'. They often occur regularly spaced, with a length-to-width ratio between 2:1 and 7:1, and are typically found in lowland areas in relative close proximity to upland centres of ice dispersal. Excellent examples of drumlin swarms occur in Northern Ireland, the Ribble Valley (Lancashire), the Cheshire Plain and North Shropshire, and Eden Valley (Cumbria).

Drumlins are an example of **equifinality** in that a number of mechanisms have been proposed for their formation, so not all drumlins are necessarily formed in the same way. Some drumlins have a rock core which also needs an explanation, whereas others do not.

- The **Boulton-Menzies theory** suggests that a drumlin is formed by deposition in the lee of a slowly moving obstacle in the deforming layer. The obstacle of bedrock, or thermally frozen material, forms the core of the drumlin and ground moraine is plastered round it.
- The **Shaw theory** suggests that all drumlins, even rock-core drumlins, were formed by subglacial meltwater in flood, causing irregularities to form in the river bed which were subsequently mouldered into drumlins, streamlined by the advancing ice.

- Recently, time lapse geophysical surveys have been carried out subglacially, and these show a drumlin forming from deforming sediments beneath the Rutford Ice Stream in West Antarctica.

In some areas, lodgement till is remoulded into streamlined **flutes**, with a length-to-width ratio in excess of 30:1. These long, narrow features are usually less than 3 m in height and less than 100 m long.

Ice-marginal moraines

Table 4 summarises the range of marginal moraines that commonly occur and suggests how they are formed. Most are linear features (L) and often form in close proximity in either lateral or terminal margin process environments.

Table 4 Marginal moraines and their formation

Type of moraine		Description	Method of formation
Lateral moraine	L	A ridge of moraine along the edge of the valley floor	Exposed rock on the valley side is weathered and fragments fall down on to the edge of the glacier. This is then carried along the valley and deposited when the ice melts. Parallel to ice flow
Medial moraine	L	A ridge of moraine down the middle of the valley floor	When two valley glaciers converge, two lateral moraines combine to form a medial. Material is carried and deposited when melting occurs. Parallel to ice flow
Terminal or end moraine	L	A ridge of moraine extending across the valley at the furthest point that the glacier reached	Advancing ice carries moraine forward and deposits it at the point of maximum advance when it retreats. The up-valley (ice contact) side is generally steeper than the other side as the advancing ice rose over the debris. Transverse to ice flow
Recessional moraine	L	A series of ridges running across the valley behind the terminal moraine	Each recessional moraine, and there may be many, represents a stillstand during ice retreat. They are good indicators of the cycle of advance and retreat that many glaciers experience. Transverse to ice flow
Push moraine	L	A ridge of moraine with stones tilted upwards	Any morainic material at the glacier snout will be pushed forward during advance. The faster the velocity of advance, the steeper the angle of tilt or stones. Transverse to ice flow
Hummocky or disintegration moraine	NL	Chaotic jumble of till mounds	Originally considered a product of ice stagnation and dropped from a debris-rich glacier, now associated with active glacial retreat. Limited orientation

L, linear; NL, non-linear.

These glacial depositional landforms are difficult to analyse as they are frequently interspersed with features of fluvioglacial deposition. Moreover, as glaciers advance and retreat, or stand still, they often rework older glacial deposits into new forms, adding to the complexity of depositional landforms.

As well as creating distinctive landscapes in both lowland areas such as eastern Denmark, and in the floors of glaciated valleys, glacial depositional landforms help glaciologists understand not only the extent of ice cover, but also its provenance. In some cases it is the orientation of the feature, in others it is the contrasting up-glacier (stoss) and down-glacier shape (lee), and in yet others it is the actual debris that yields the clues. The overall geography of the assemblage of features is also important, in particular behind and in front of any terminal morainic ridges, as these mark glacial snouts or ice sheet edges.

Knowledge check 11

State three ways in which you could distinguish morainic features to identify which type they are.

Knowledge check 12

Explain how the provenance of ice can be established by studying glacial depositional features.

Glacier hydrology: the role of meltwater

Meltwater from glaciers plays a vital role in the processes of erosion, entrainment and transport, as well as deposition. It is indirectly involved in the processes of glacial abrasion and plucking, but it is particularly important in glacier movement by basal sliding and subglacial bed deformation (see p. 17). Meltwater beneath a glacier is also responsible for erosion as, because of its fast speed and power, it can scour and groove the underlying rock.

There are two main sources of meltwater from glaciers: **surface melting** and **basal melting**. Surface melting contributes most of the supply, peaks in late summer and is the only source of meltwater for cold basal glaciers. **Supraglacial** surface streams form, running along the top of the ice, especially in the ablation zone. These supraglacial channels are often fast-flowing and they may plunge down into the ice, either through a crevasse or more commonly via a **moulin** (a cylindrical, vertical tunnel like a pothole), so becoming **englacial** streams.

As meltwater moves through a glacier it may refreeze or contribute to further melting. It may reach the base of the glacier, becoming subglacial, depending on the temperature of the ice inside the glacier.

Basal melting occurs if the temperature of the ice at the base of a glacier is at pressure melting point (in a warm-based glacier). The basal meltwater flows beneath the glacier under hydrostatic pressure and can excavate subglacial tunnels by cutting through the bedrock. The meltwater streams eventually emerge from subglacial tunnels at the glacier snout via **portals** (caves).

Fluvioglacial processes

Fluvioglacial erosion

Away from the glacier, outlet streams behave similarly to normal streams, although their discharge, sediment loads and the lack of vegetation lead to some variations in operation. However, within the glacier, **fluvioglacial streams** operate very differently because of high pressure and velocity of flow. This causes erosion of underlying bedrock by abrasion, cavitation and chemical means beneath the glacier ice, and can also cause intense erosion by meltwater streams as they exit the glacier snout. The ablation rates are high during deglaciation and many of the meltwater streams have high discharges, which can result in powerful erosion. They also form subglacial channels, see p. 31.

Fluvioglacial deposition

When meltwater deposits material subglacially, englacially and supraglacially, the material is referred to as an **ice-contact fluvioglacial deposit**. Where the fluvioglacial material is deposited at or beyond the ice margin, by streams coming out of the snout, it is known as **proglacial** or outwash deposits.

Characteristics of fluvioglacial deposits

In comparison with glacial deposits (tills), fluvioglacial deposits tend to be:

- generally smaller in size, because although meltwater streams have seasonally high discharge, they still have less energy than large valley glaciers so they generally carry finer material
- generally smoother and **rounder**, as a result of water contact and **attrition**
- **sorted** horizontally, especially in the case of outwash deposition, with the largest material found up-valley, or nearer the glacier snout, and progressively finer material down-valley, because of the **sequential** nature of the deposition mechanisms
- **stratified** vertically, with distinctive layers that reflect either seasonal or annual sediment accumulation

A further distinction can be made between **ice-contact fluvioglacial** deposits and **outwash deposits**. Outwash deposits experience more **attrition**, causing clasts to become more rounded, and the material is better sorted horizontally.

Knowledge check 13

Explain four major differences between glacial and fluvioglacial deposits.

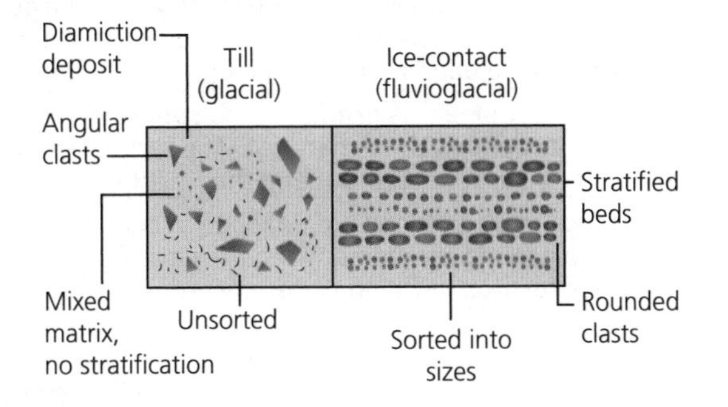

Figure 10 The differences between glacial and fluvioglacial deposits

Three main zones of outwash deposition extend from the front of the glacier, and the characteristics change through these zones.

The **proximal zone** is immediately in front of the glacier, close to the snout. The meltwater has the greatest power, so outwash deposits contain large particles. Outwash may be interbedded with layers of till, as some glacial deposition may occur. Outwash may occur in alluvial fan forms.

The **medial zone** is further from the ice margin. Meltwater streams tend to anastomose and form braided channels because of high daily and seasonal variability of meltwater discharge. Particle size is less coarse and clasts are more rounded.

The **distal zone** is furthest from the ice margin. The drainage pattern resembles a normal drainage system, with meanders on a broad floodplain. Outwash is well sorted and characterised by smaller and even more rounded particles.

Fluvioglacial landforms

Subglacial meltwater can excavate large meltwater channels. These can cut across contours as the direction of the meltwater flow is controlled by the hydrostatic pressure gradient. Subglacial meltwater can even flow uphill so these channels can have 'humped' long profiles. Examples of these meltwater channels can be found in many parts of the UK, including the Gwaun Valley in North Pembrokeshire.

Table 5 The main landforms of fluvioglacial deposition

	Landform	Appearance	Formation
Ice contact	Eskers	Long, sinuous ridges on the valley floor	Material is deposited in subglacial tunnels as the supply of meltwater decreases at the end of the glacial period. Subglacial streams may carry huge amounts of debris under pressure in the confined tunnel in the base of the ice
	Delta kames	Small mounds on the valley floor	Englacial streams emerging at the snout of the glacier fall to the valley floor, lose energy and deposit their load *Or* Supraglacial streams deposit material on entering ice-marginal lakes
	Kame terraces	Ridges of material running along the edge of the valley floor	Supraglacial streams on the edge of the glacier pick up and carry lateral moraine, which is then deposited on the valley floor as the glacier retreats
Proglacial	Varves	Layers of sediment found at the bottom of lakes	Sediment carried by meltwater streams is deposited on entering a lake as energy is lost. In summer, when large amounts of meltwater are available, the sediment is coarse and plentiful, leading to a wide band of sediment of relatively large material. In winter, with little meltwater present, sediment is limited in amount and size and so bands are thin and fine
	Outwash (sandur)	A flat expanse of sediment in the proglacial area	As meltwater streams gradually lose energy on entering lowland areas, they deposit their material. The largest material is deposited nearest the snout and the finest further away
	Kettle holes	Small circular lakes in outwash plains	During ice retreat, blocks of dead ice become detached. Sediment builds up around them and when they eventually melt a small hollow is formed in which water accumulates to form a lake

Ice-contact features

- **Eskers** result from subglacial meltwater deposition. They are sinuous ridges of relatively coarse sand and gravel deposited by meltwater flowing through tunnels, sometimes englacially but normally subglacially. Eskers have a variety of sizes — a small esker is found at Wark on the River Tweed in the UK — it is about 1 km long, 40 m wide and about 20 m high. Some eskers are **beaded** — they have a number of wider parts that resemble a string of beads, possibly marking stillstands of the ice front.

  Eskers are thought to occur when a subglacial or englacial channel becomes obstructed, leading to deposition of material upstream from the blockage. For englacial eskers to form, the ice needs to be stagnant — otherwise the material would be reworked by glacier ice movement. Another possible mode of formation is where a delta of fluvioglacial material extends outward, perpendicular to the ice margin, taking on an elongated form under conditions of rapid ice retreat.
- **Kames** are generally steep-sided conical hills, although they take a variety of shapes and sizes. They are formed by deposition of material in ice, either in surface depressions or crevasses, or alternatively as deltas along the sides of a glacier between the ice margin and the hillside. They show some evidence of stratification although the bedding can be disturbed by subsidence as the ice melts away.
- **Kame terraces** form relatively continuous bench-like features along the valley side, when a gap or a lake between the valley side and the ice margin is filled with fluvioglacial deposits.

Exam tip

Use Table 5 as a basis and research examples of the key features.

Knowledge check 14

Equifinality is a concept that can be applied to esker formation. Explain this term.

- Some regions of extensive kame deposits also contain **kettle holes** (see below) and can be described as areas of **kame and kettle topography**. This usually develops when there is a large amount of fluvioglacial material deposited over the surface of stagnant ice, which melts in situ.

Proglacial features

When an englacial or subglacial stream exits the snout of a glacier there is a rapid decrease in water pressure and velocity, causing the deposition of coarse fluvioglacial material as an **outwash fan**. Outwash fans merge to become part of a debris-rich, anastomosing braided drainage system. As the discharge of meltwater decreases with deglaciation, the broad expanse of fluvioglacial material that was deposited and spread out by the braided river systems is left behind as an outwash plain or **sandur**. An outwash plain is a gently sloping surface made up of rounded, sorted and stratified sands and gravels, with the particle size becoming progressively smaller away from the ice front.

Outwash plains may contain **kettle holes** where any surviving blocks of ice during deglaciation were buried by **outwash** material. After the ice melted, the ground above it subsided, leading to formation of a depression which subsequently filled with water. As these kettle holes are only fed by rainwater, many of the smaller ones are gradually colonised by vegetation (hydroseres) and subsequently dry up. In the Ellesmere area of north Shropshire there is any area with many kettle holes varying from 400 m to 1.5 km in size.

Knowledge check 15

Explain why kettle holes can vary in size.

Proglacial lakes (also known as ice-margin lakes) are formed along the front of glaciers and ice sheets where meltwater exiting from the glacier becomes impounded within a depression blocked by glacier ice and bounded by high ground (Figure 11).

These lakes are ephemeral (temporary) features because, depending on the rapidity of deglaciation, the proglacial lake can empty completely usually via a pre-existing col, or can stabilise at a lower level if the ice margin has not completely disappeared.

The dimensions of former proglacial lakes can be inferred from both erosional and depositional forms. The parallel roads of Glen Roy in the Scottish Highlands mark a series of former **strandlines** of a proglacial lake formed during the Loch Lomond stadial. Strandlines, which mark the shore of the proglacial lake, may occur if the water level was stationary for a relatively long time. It also may be possible to find former lake deltas, where meltwater streams deposited outwash as they entered the lake. If the water was relatively calm in the lake, **varved** deposits would form. They are characterised by alternate bands of relatively coarse-grained sand, reflecting the rapid ice melt in summer at the base of the layer, overlain by fine, dark-coloured silt or clay that came out of suspension when the lake's surface and the streams that fed it were frozen in winter. These annual bands of sediment reflect the seasonal variation in discharge from the glacier.

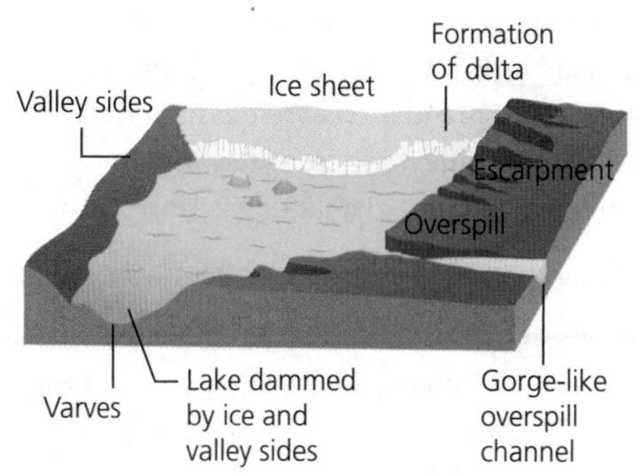

Figure 11 The formation of a proglacial lake

Proglacial lakes were a common feature in the Pleistocene, with many forming in the English Midlands, such as Lake Harrison or Lake Lapworth. Many proglacial lakes were enormous, such as those formed along the margins of the Laurentide Ice Sheet in North America, for example Lake Agassiz covered an area of around 300,000 km^2 at its maximum. The draining of Lake Agassiz is cited as a possible feedback mechanism for the onset of the Loch Lomond stadial.

Overflow channels, also known as meltwater spillways, are formed when proglacial lakes overflow their confines. These channels are an open V shape, often gorge-like and sinuous, as they were caused by intense fluvial erosion along an outflow path. Many of these channels are now dry or contain only a small (misfit) stream. These overflow channels can lead to diversions of pre-glacial drainage systems.

Summary

- Glacial and fluvioglacial transport includes supraglacial, englacial and subglacial processes.
- Different processes produce different types of till. Glacial, as opposed to fluvioglacial, deposits tend to be angular, unsorted and unstratified.
- Landforms of glacial deposition include types of till (ablation, lodgement and deformation), types of moraine (terminal, recessional, lateral, medial and push) and drumlins.
- Fluvioglacial transport and deposition results in ice-contact features such as eskers, kames and kame terraces, and proglacial features such as sandurs, varves, kettle holes and kettle lakes.

Glacial landscapes and their landforms

This section looks at the bigger picture to explore how suites of landforms contribute to a variety of glacial landscapes, for example within various regions of Scotland.

There are contrasting landscapes between highland and lowland areas and the types of ice mass. In general, highland areas are source regions of glaciers and ice caps, and therefore sites of classic glaciated highland scenery. Lowland areas tend to be areas of slower-moving or stagnant ice and are therefore major sites of both glacial and fluvioglacial deposition, including proglacial features beyond the glacier snout. Highland areas are characterised by significant ice erosion with characteristic U-shaped valleys whereas lowland ones, such as the Tweed Valley, have a full range of fluvioglacial and glacial deposition features.

The situation is complex, as yet other areas were not covered by ice and therefore were subject to periglacial conditions resulting in another suite of landforms (see pp. 39–41).

Fundamental reasons for the variety of glaciated landscape include the erosive power of the ice, which is linked to a variety of glacier features; whether the glacier is warm-based or cold-based (see p. 14); and how thick the ice is, which will affect its rate of movement and therefore its erosive power. Of more local importance is the geology, density of jointing, hardness of rock and the topography (availability of existing routes and cols, and the slope angle).

Exam tip

Illustrate specific landscapes with a series of complete diagrams. Use the diagrams and examples from the UK and beyond to support your work. Use the checklist on p. 23. You should also download maps of your chosen areas.

Landscapes of highland glaciation from valley glaciers

Figure 12 shows the classic features associated with **highland glaciations** by alpine or valley glaciers. Moving ice masses, and hence their erosional forces, are concentrated in valleys to form glacial troughs. These valley glaciers are either outlet glaciers fed from ice caps or ice fields, or originate in one or more ice-accumulation sources at the valley head, i.e. a series of cirque glaciers.

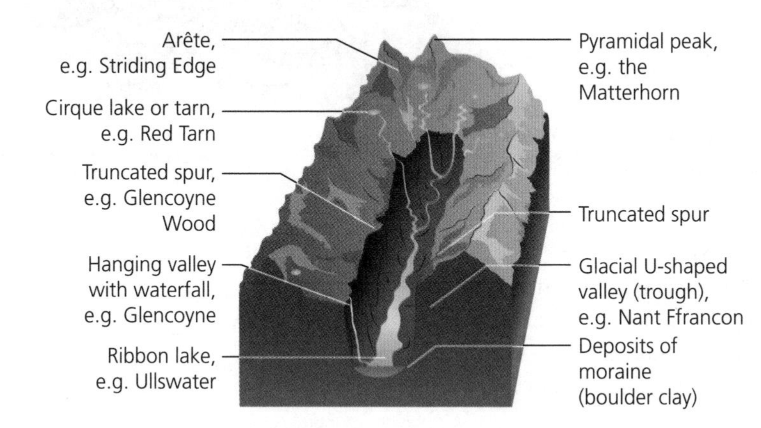

Figure 12 The features associated with highland glaciation

The long and cross profiles of glacial troughs are important. Some glacial troughs have a strongly developed U shape, such as Lauterbrunnen in Switzerland, but the majority have a broader parabolic cross-section carved as ice masses widened, deepened and straightened pre-existing river valleys — with the thickest and most erosive ice found in the centre of the valley. Other local factors such as geology also play a part, for example the Buttermere–Crummock trough in the English Lake District is asymmetrical because of the differential resistance of rocks on the two flanks of the glacier.

Glaciated highland landscapes can be described using a structure that takes into account all elements of the landscape:

- the landscape at source, for example, corries, arêtes and pyramidal peaks
- features of the glacial trough, such as hanging valleys, truncated spurs and ribbon lakes
- depositional features, such as recessional moraines
- micro features, such as striations, chatter marks or erratics
- periglacial features, where the valley sides were not covered by ice, such as relict stone stripes, tors, screes, i.e. above the **trim line**
- post-glacial modifications, such as fluvial erosion by misfit streams or the development of alluvial fans from hanging valleys etc., as well as infilling of ribbon lakes and the modification of drainage patterns

As valley glaciers moved into lowland areas, some went only a little way beyond their sources, especially during late-stage glaciation such as the Loch Lomond stadial, whereas others coalesced to form lowland ice sheets, so developing a full suite of glacial and fluvioglacial depositional features.

Exam tip

Always support your answer with detailed exemplification — three concise sentences work well — and also use your fieldwork experience.

Landscapes formed by ice sheets

Ice sheets can form in both highland and lowland areas, resulting in contrasting landscapes.

Ice sheet erosion

Erosion beneath an ice sheet varies widely. Key variables that affect this include ice thickness, speed of movement and, particularly, the temperature regime of the ice sheet (warm- or cold-based). The underlying relief, geology and how long the ice sheet cover lasted are also significant. The most common type of ice sheet erosion is **aerial scouring**, which produces a landscape of low-lying, flattish, ice-smoothed hills, as shown in Figure 13.

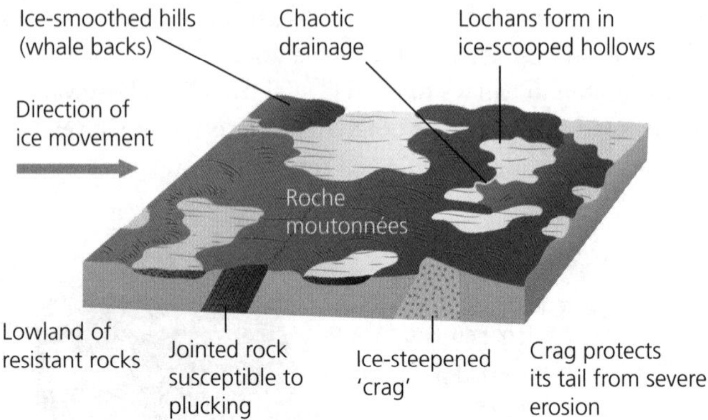

Figure 13 Lowland glaciation erosion

This type of landscape is associated with extensive coverage by warm-based ice that is quite slow-moving, which differentially eroded the hard bedrock. Therefore the structure of the underlying rock has a major impact on the orientation and scale of the erosional landforms. The landscape consists of extensive tracts of subglacially eroded bedrock, composed of many whale backs, roches moutonnées and overdeepened rock basins.

In northwest Scotland (Sutherland and the Isle of Lewis) the landscape is called **knock and lochan topography** because the higher areas of resistant rock (knocks) are interspersed with numerous small lakes in the rock basin (lochans). A **chaotic** drainage pattern has resulted, often where patches of residual moraine interfere with the drainage. Landscapes of areal scour also occur in the Central Finland Lake Belt and the Canadian Shield, both areas of ancient resistant igneous and metamorphic rocks where differential erosion is controlled by density of jointing. These areas may also contain examples of **crag and tail** (meso-scale landforms, see p. 25).

Work in Antarctica has confirmed that ice sheets did not create the overall landforms of the great shield areas, which had acquired their almost level surfaces by denudation pre-Ice Age. These ice sheets did, however, considerably modify the underlying surface over which they passed, confirmed by the generally low amplitude of relief (less than 100 m) with many meso- and micro-scale features.

Different landscapes result where the ice sheets are cold-based. Where upland plateaux are covered with thin ice sheets with little or no basal load there is limited glacial erosion, as in the Cairngorms plateau, or West Greenland on Baffin Island (Canada). The landscape tends to have a weathered debris mantle, with gentle slopes and scattered blockfields of erratics, or occasional tors, as in Arctic Canada.

Ice sheet deposition

Ice sheet deposition occurs when numerous ice sources coalesce to form huge ice sheets which, because of the relief, are very slow-moving or stagnant (i.e. at a **stillstand**), for example over much of lowland England such as Yorkshire and the English Midlands, or over the continent of Europe including most of Denmark, southern Sweden and the North European plain, as well as southern Canada and northern USA.

Knowledge check 16

Distinguish between landform and landscape.

Inevitably there are a series of depositional features (see Figure 14) that occur before and in front of the significant terminal moraines that mark the edge of the ice sheet. As there was often a series of readvances, stillstands and ultimately recessions at the ice sheet front, the features found in the landscape are complex.

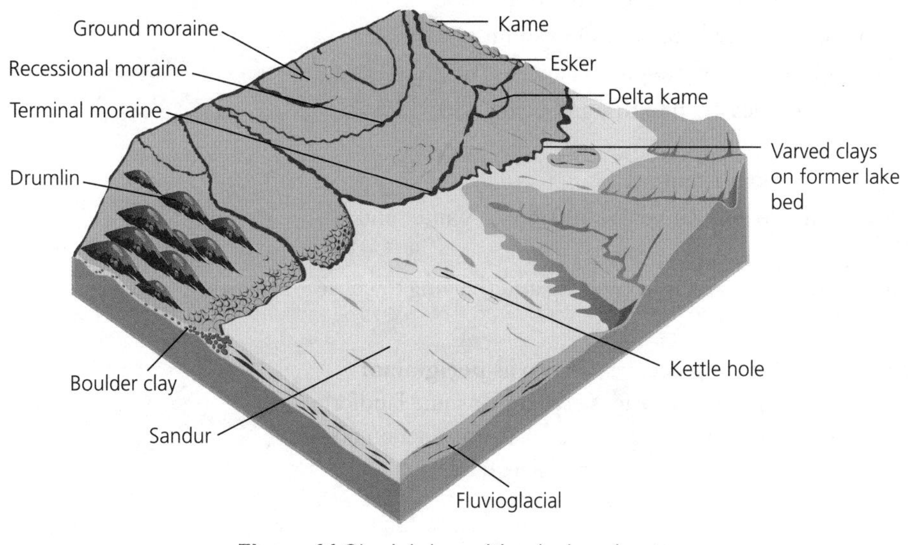

Figure 14 Glacial deposition by ice sheets

Summary

- Glacial landscapes vary between highland and lowland areas, and between areas with ice sheets and those with valley glaciers.
- Highland areas have classic glaciated highland scenery with characteristic U-shaped valleys, whereas lowland areas tend to show glacial and fluvioglacial deposition, including proglacial features.
- The type of ice sheet landscape depends on the erosive power of the ice, whether the glacier is warm- or cold-based, how thick the ice is, its rate of movement, and the geology, density of jointing, hardness of rock and topography.
- The most common form of ice sheet erosion (warm-based) is aerial scouring, which produces a landscape of low-lying, flattish, ice-smoothed hills. Cold-based ice sheets produce limited glacial erosion, and landscapes with a weathered debris mantle, gentle slopes and scattered blockfields of erratics.
- Ice sheet depositional landscapes include features such as moraines, outwash plains, kettle holes, drumlins and eskers.

Periglacial processes and the formation of associated features

Periglacial environments

The term **periglacial** has traditionally referred to the climate conditions and landscape that characterised areas near the margins of glacier ice during the Pleistocene, or temporally before the onset of glacial conditions. However, the term is now more widely used to include all non-glacial cold climate areas with a wide range of different high-latitude and high-altitude environments which may or may not contain glaciers.

Periglacial climates typically have many of the following characteristics:

- intense frosts during winter and on any snow-free ground in summer
- highest average annual temperatures usually between 1°C and −4°C
- daily temperatures are below 0°C for at least 9 months, and below −10°C for at least 6 months per year
- temperatures rarely rise above 18°C, even in summer
- low precipitation, typically less than 600 mm per year (<100 mm in winter and <500 mm in summer)
- temperatures fluctuating through frequent cycles of freezing and thawing to cause **interstitial ice** (ice within cracks) to melt

These climate conditions give rise to a variety of processes, known as **periglacial** processes, which combine to produce distinctive landscapes containing some landforms that are unique to periglacial areas. However, some processes such as frost action occur quite widely elsewhere, although with less intensity than in periglacial areas.

Permafrost

Permafrost is often loosely defined as 'permanently frozen ground', but technically the term refers to soil and rock that remain frozen because temperatures do not exceed 0°C in the summer months for at least two consecutive years.

- **Continuous permafrost** (see Figure 15) forms in the coldest areas of the world where mean annual air temperatures are below −6°C. It can extend downwards for hundreds of metres.
- **Discontinuous permafrost** is more fragmented and thinner.
- **Sporadic permafrost** occurs at the margins of periglacial environments and is usually fragmented and only a few metres thick, often occurring on shady hillsides or beneath peat.

Knowledge check 17

Explain the difference between periglacial conditions and permafrost.

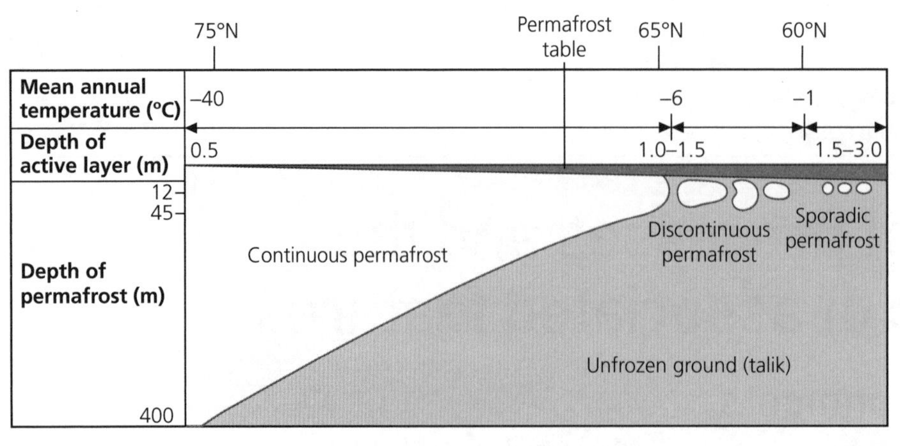

Figure 15 Cross-section of permafrost areas

In summer, the energy balance is positive, which causes overlying snow and ice to melt away to produce a seasonally unfrozen zone above the permafrost called the active layer, which varies from a few centimetres to as deep as 3.0 m.

Up to 25% of the Earth's surface is currently experiencing permafrost conditions, especially in the northern hemisphere (Siberia and almost 50% of Canada, 80% of Alaska). While periglacial environments usually contain permafrost, sometimes areas of periglacial activity involving intense frost action do exist outside the permafrost zone.

A number of factors influence the distribution and character of permafrost:

- Climate is the main control, as temperature and the amount of moisture available determine the presence or absence, depth and extent of permafrost.
- On a local scale, the depth and extent of permafrost is influenced by a number of interrelated factors:
  - proximity to water bodies is important — as lakes are relatively warm they will remain unfrozen throughout the year and have a deep active layer
  - slope angle and orientation influence the amount of solar radiation and therefore melting, freeze–thaw and wind
  - character of the ground surface (different rock and soil types) can determine the degree and depth of permafrost, e.g. dark compact rocks absorb more solar radiation
  - vegetation cover can insulate the ground from temperature extremes
  - snow cover can slow the freezing process in winter and delay the thaw and development of the active layer in spring

In conclusion, the depth of permafrost formation is affected by energy balance at the surface, thermal characteristics of subsurface material and geothermal heat flow from below.

Periglacial processes and landforms

Cold climate environments develop distinctive geomorphology because of four basic processes:

1. The expansion of water by 9% on freezing. This causes frost shattering, which forms block fields and screes.
2. The contraction and cracking of rapidly freezing soils, which results in the formation of ice wedges, as well as frost heaving which creates patterned ground.
3. The migration of subsurface water to the 'freezing front' by suction, which causes the formation of segregated ice leading to the formation of ice lens, palsas and pingos.
4. The mass movement of the active layer downslope, largely by **solifluction**, which creates lobes and terraces.

Of these processes, only frost shattering occurs outside periglacial areas. The other three processes are associated with permafrost, and melting and movements within the active layer could be considered unique to periglacial environments. As Figure 16 shows there are also other processes, such as wind and fluvial action, which are prevalent but not exclusive to periglacial areas.

Knowledge check 18

Define the term 'solifluction'.

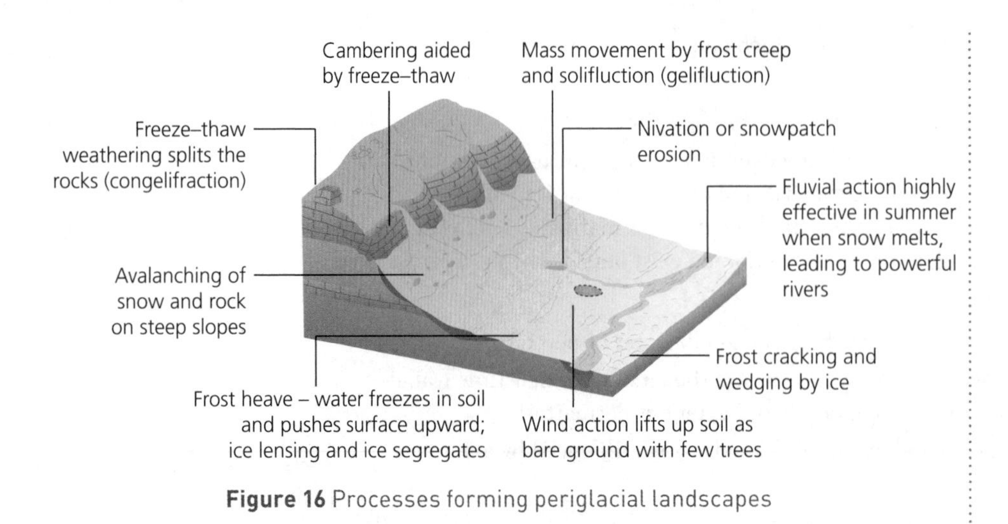

Figure 16 Processes forming periglacial landscapes

Ground ice features

Major ground ice features include the following:

1 Networks of **ice wedge polygons**, which are unique to periglacial areas. The process of frost cracking creates areas of irregular polygons, usually 5–30 m across, mostly found on valley floors. When the active layer thaws, ice wedges can begin to form as water flows into the cracks during the thaw and subsequently freezes and contracts, which means the ice wedge can build up over time. The larger ice wedges are usually a tapering shape, 1–2 m wide and up to 10 m deep extending down into the permafrost, taking more than 100 years to form.

2 **Patterned ground** (Figure 17) is the general term for a range of features that include circles, nets, polygons, steps and stripes. These features are unique to periglacial areas, and are formed by a series of movements resulting from frost action. **Frost push** propels stones upwards, and **frost heave** causes stones to migrate outwards to form circles, which provide the basis for each of the other patterns. The up-doming of the circle created by heave means that larger stones roll outwards due to gravity, while finer sediments remain in the centre. Mass movement causes stone polygons to become elongated into **stone nets** and **stripes**, with a clear relationship between slope angle and the type of patterned ground. Once slope gradients increase beyond 30°, patterned ground features no longer form and rock avalanches may occur.

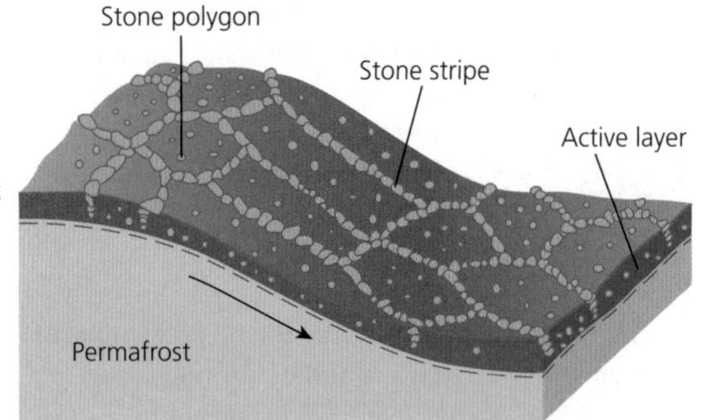

Figure 17 Patterned ground

3 Large **ice lenses** may slowly build up in soil that is frozen when water migrates to the 'freezing front' in permafrost regions.

4 **Pingos** are a unique periglacial feature. They are ice core mounds 30–70 m in height and 100–500 m in diameter. The mounds can be either conical or elongated. The growth of an ice core forces up the overlying sediments causing **dilation cracks**. Once the ice core is exposed at the surface it melts, causing the

top of the pingo to collapse, so forming a crater that may be filled with meltwater and sediments. Two types of pingo occur:

i Open system pingos (hydraulic or East Greenland type) are found in the discontinuous zone of permafrost or valley floors. Freely available groundwater is drawn towards the expanding ice core, so the pingo grows from *below* the ground.

ii Closed system pingos (hydrostatic pingos or Mackenzie delta type) are associated with low-lying flat areas and form only in zones of continuous permafrost. They form from the *downward* growth of permafrost, often after a small lake is gradually enclosed with sediments. The loss of the insulating influence of the lake allows permafrost to advance, so trapping the body of water and putting it under hydrostatic pressure and ultimately freezing, to push up the sediment above it.

Frost weathering and mass movement

The role of frost shattering

Freeze–thaw weathering puts pressure on cracks in rocks and shatters them. While the process is not unique to periglacial environments it occurs with greater severity within them.

The features created by freeze–thaw include:

- **block fields** (felsenmeer or 'rock seas') are accumulations of angular, frost-shattered rock, which pile up on flat plateau surfaces. They form in situ, created by frost heaving of jointed bedrock and freeze–thaw weathering
- **tors** with 'crown' hill tops stand out from block fields. They form where more resistant areas of rock occur — for example, less well-jointed rock
- **scree** or **talus stopes** are formed when rock fragments fall and accumulate on the lower slopes or base of cliffs. The larger the material that makes up the slope the steeper it will be
- **protalus ramparts** are created if a patch of snow has settled at the base of a cliff. When rocks fall, as they are shattered by frost action, the snow patch acts as a buffer so the rocks settle at the base of the snow patch, leaving a rampart of boulders when the snow melts
- **rock glaciers** form when large amounts of frost-shattered rock mixes with ice. On the surface rock glaciers look like streams or fans of angular rocks, but they are conjoined with interstitial ice below and move slowly, like glaciers, at rates of up to 1 m a year.

The role of mass movement

Frost creep and solifluction are the most important mass movement processes acting on slopes in periglacial environments.

- **Frost creep** is a slow form of mass movement, which moves material downslope by just a few centimetres per year, even on steeper slopes.
- **Solifluction** occurs in regions underlain by permafrost. During the summer months the active layer melts, forming a mobile water-saturated layer which results in the formation of either stone-banked or turf-banked **lobes** on slopes of 10° to 20°. Terraces or benches occur on more gentle slopes. The deposits that result collect in the bottom of periglacial valleys and are known as head or coombe rock.

Analysis of **clasts** (stones within the deposits) shows downslope orientation and both angular and subangular shapes.

- **Asymmetric valleys** occur in periglacial environments. Differential rates of solifluction and frost creep result in one side of the valley becoming significantly steeper than the other. For example, in the northern hemisphere, south-facing slopes receive more insolation and thaw more frequently, thus increasing soil moisture and promoting mass movement, resulting in a less steep slope. Many of these valleys now occur as **dry valleys** as they were occupied by meltwater streams in the periglacial period.

You will often find '**head**' deposits, which result from solifluction, in the floor of an asymmetric valley.

The role of snow

The localised process of **nivation** occurs when both frost weathering and erosion take place around and beneath a snow patch. It is a common process in periglacial areas and leads to **nivation hollows** forming at the base of a slope (these can initiate the formation of **cirques**).

Periglacial action of water and wind

The role of wind and meltwater rivers

Many periglacial areas are extremely arid, because much of the water is frozen and not available for plant growth (a **physiological drought**). The absence of vegetation provides abundant opportunities for wind action. In the Pleistocene Ice Ages, deposits of fine silt-sized sediment formed on the extensive outwash plains (**sandurs**) from the great European and North American ice sheets, were blown southwards and deposited as **loess**. Loess plateaux cover large areas of Europe and North America, forming rich soils.

Water erosion in periglacial areas is highly seasonal, occurring mainly in spring and early summer, when surface snow and ice and the active layer melt, leading to short periods of very high meltwater stream discharge. Near the margins of glaciers the drainage pattern is typically **braided** (sometimes called **anastomosing**) because of the high amount of debris being carried by meltwater streams.

Periglacial environments contain some unique landforms and some that can be found more widely, such as loess plateaux and braided drainage. It is the assembly of these landforms within a tundra slope catena, and the occurrence of tundra ecosystems and soils, which creates the distinctive landscapes characteristic of periglacial environments.

Relict periglacial features

When the climate warms, periglacial features can form distinctive relict forms. In **paraglacial** conditions (non-glacial environments conditioned by previous glaciations) just after the rapid melting of permafrost, a **thermokarst** landscape can occur, so called because the depressions reminded scientists of the sink holes

Exam tip

Periglacial environments are part of wider cold environments. You need to be clear how they relate to glacial environments.

Knowledge check 19

Make a table to list all the periglacial landforms which you consider to be unique.

Knowledge check 20

Explain the term 'relict periglacial feature'.

found in limestone (karst) landscapes. This landscape contains large areas of surface depressions and irregularly shaped lakes.

However, in areas such as the UK it is only comparatively recently that many 'mystery' features have been attributed to the periglacial conditions experienced during the last ice age, often by surveying areas of present-day periglaciation.

Summary

- In ground ice, frost action and ice build-up results in features such as ice wedge polygons, patterned ground, pingos and ice lenses.
- Frost weathering and mass movement result in features such as blockfields and scree slopes, protalus ramparts, solifluction terraces and head deposits and nivation hollows (under snow).
- Frost creep and solifluction are the most important mass movement processes acting on slopes in periglacial environments, causing features such as stone-banked or turf-banked lobes, terraces or benches and asymmetric valleys, many of which are now dry.
- Periglacial action of water and wind forms braided drainage and loess plateaux.
- Thermokarst landscapes (relict features) with large areas of surface depressions and irregularly shaped lakes occur after rapid melting of permafrost.

Variations in glacial processes and landforms over time

Table 6 shows the variety of temporal scales linked to glacial processes and landforms.

Table 6 Temporal scale of glacial processes and landforms

	Timescale	Process and landforms
Rapid	Seconds, minutes, weekly	Mass movement such as rock falls, avalanches, glacial outburst floods and overflows from proglacial lakes
	Seasonal Annual	Changes in accumulation and ablation Flows of meltwater streams and sediment deposition Changes in permafrost — depth of active layer Changes in net balance of glacier (positive or negative)
	Decadal Centennial	Trends and balance of glaciers (cumulative changes) Impacts of global warming on glacier size
Slow	Millennial	Formation of features resulting from sea level change Occurrence of stadials such as Little Ice Age Post-glacial modification of glaciated areas by fluvial action
	Millions of years	Pleistocene Ice Age with glacials and interglacials, i.e. ice house–greenhouse conditions

Rapid changes in glacial processes and landforms

Both current and relict glaciated upland regions are hazardous because of the high incidence of avalanches, rock falls, debris slides and flooding. These hazards can develop into disasters because of the increasing human vulnerability in these areas, resulting from increasing population and development as well as the growing popularity of outdoor sports and adventure tourism which put more people at risk. They can occur almost instantaneously, so adding to the hazard.

Avalanches

An avalanche risk exists when shear stress exceeds shear strength of a mass of snow located on a slope. The shear strength of a snow pack is related to its density and temperature. Snow avalanches result from two different types of snow pack failure:

1. **Loose snow** acts like dry sand. A small amount of snow slips out of place and starts to move down-slope.
2. **Slab avalanches** occur when a strongly cohesive layer of snow breaks away from a weaker underlying layer. A period of higher temperatures followed by refreezing creates ice crusts, which are a source of instability. Slabs can be as large as 100,000 m^3 and this slab ice can bring down more than a hundred times the initial volume of snow and cause huge danger.

Knowledge check 21

Explain why avalanches can lead to disasters under certain conditions.

Most avalanches start with a gliding motion then rapidly accelerate, especially on steep slopes in excess of 30°. Three types of avalanche motion commonly occur:

1. **powder** avalanches — the most hazardous
2. **dry flow** avalanches
3. **wet flow** avalanches, which occur mainly in spring

While avalanches tend to follow well-known tracks and can often be predicted, they are nevertheless a significant hazard, usually killing around 200 people per year. Most of these deaths happen in the Alps or the Rockies. The recent 2015 Nepalese earthquake set off many **ice and rock avalanches**, which killed scores of climbers about to begin Everest ascents.

As well as being hazardous, rock and debris avalanches modify the shape of the glaciated valley, changing it from a parabolic cross-section. Occasionally, debris dams or landslides can create temporary lakes in a U-shaped valley.

Lahars

Volcanic activity can cause large-scale glacier melting, resulting in some of the most destructive volcanic hazard events, **lahars** (mudflows). The second deadliest eruption recorded in historic times was the 1985 eruption of Nevado del Ruiz, Colombia. The eruption caused large-scale melting of the glacier, producing a huge lahar which rushed down the Lagunillas Valley, overwhelming the town of Armero, 50 km downstream. With a mudflow deposit of 3–8 m deep it killed more than 23,000 people almost instantly. See Figure 38 on p. 79.

Another example of a rapidly occurring event is glacial outburst flooding, see p. 47.

Seasonal variations in processes and landform change

Meltwater is an obvious example of a seasonal change in water flow and subsequent deposition, as the ability of a river to transport debris is linked to its discharge level.

From spring onwards, especially in warm-based glaciers, the discharge of glacial meltwater streams begins to increase as the glacier's ablation rate increases, and this continues until late autumn, with a summer peak. This has the following impacts:

- In summer, the supraglacial, englacial and subglacial streams are able to transport more load (a greater capacity) and they are also be able to move boulders and cobbles of larger sizes (calibre). They carry out more work and, in doing so, there is greater corrasion and attrition, so rounding the clasts. As these streams reach the ice front in summer, they carry huge quantities of load, some of which is morainic material that is reworked. Proglacially the meltwaters are responsible for both horizontal grading and vertical stratification (see p. 31).
- In winter time, when there is less discharge from the fluvioglacial streams, only comparatively fine material will be moved (if any).

Clear stratification can be seen in sections of fluvioglacial material as a result of seasonality of flow.

Another example is seen in the beds of proglacial lakes, where debris is brought down to the lake. In summer, coarse debris (sands and gravels) is dumped, but in winter only the fine material carried down in suspension is deposited and this finally settles to produce **varved** deposits with alternate fine and coarse material (see p. 33).

Millennial or long-term processes and landform change

In **relict** glaciated areas, the last period of glaciation was around 11,500 years ago (the Loch Lomond readvance in the UK). Since then, a number of processes have been responsible for post-glacial modification, including frost action, mass movement and fluvial processes operating over thousands of years.

Figure 18 illustrates these post-glacial processes for a cirque.

- Frost shattering on the cirque wall has caused fresh rock avalanches — fresh screes overlie the relict screes of the glacial period, which have been steadily vegetated over.
- A lake or tarn formed in the cirque and this has been gradually infilled, with some reworked glacial debris from the moraines around the lake as well as lacustrine silt.
- The morainic ridge, formed in glacial times, has been breached by the Nant y Llyn stream, which has begun to rework the moraine deposits and carry them down the valley.
- Peat has colonised the badly drained moraine area.

The post-glacial modifications also continue in the main U-shaped valley.

- Depending on the altitude and aspect of the area, current frost weathering processes take place on the tops and sides of the glaciated valleys, forming extensive scree deposits on the valley sides, for example of Wastwater in the Lake District.
- Ribbon lakes are gradually infilled, often from alluvial fans from sidestreams issuing from hanging valleys. The more shallow and smaller lakes are more likely to be infilled and some have completely disappeared, leaving mostly alluvial flats. Interlaken in Switzerland is built on an alluvial flat built out to divide a larger

Exam tip

A useful case study is the Grand Teton and Yellowstone glaciation in the USA. Jackson Hole in Wyoming provides an excellent example of how glacial erosion, glacial deposition and meltwater action all combine to alter the drainage patterns over the millennium and even longer-term timescales.

lake into two (see p. 24). Many glaciated valleys contain misfit streams, where a comparatively small post-glacial stream meanders across the floor of a wide, deep glaciated valley.

Kettle holes (see p. 32), a proglacial feature, frequently infill — a good example of hydrosere succession. They are fed only by rainwater and so steadily evaporate.

One of the main post-glacial impacts is how drainage adjusts to the changes brought about by the ice.

- **Proglacial lakes** drain to cause overflow channels.
- Ice **diffluence** of pre-existing watersheds, or the creation of glacial overflow channels or spillways, have all diverted drainage systems from their pre-glacial direction of flow.

Knowledge check 22

Distinguish between ice diffluence channels and proglacial spillways.

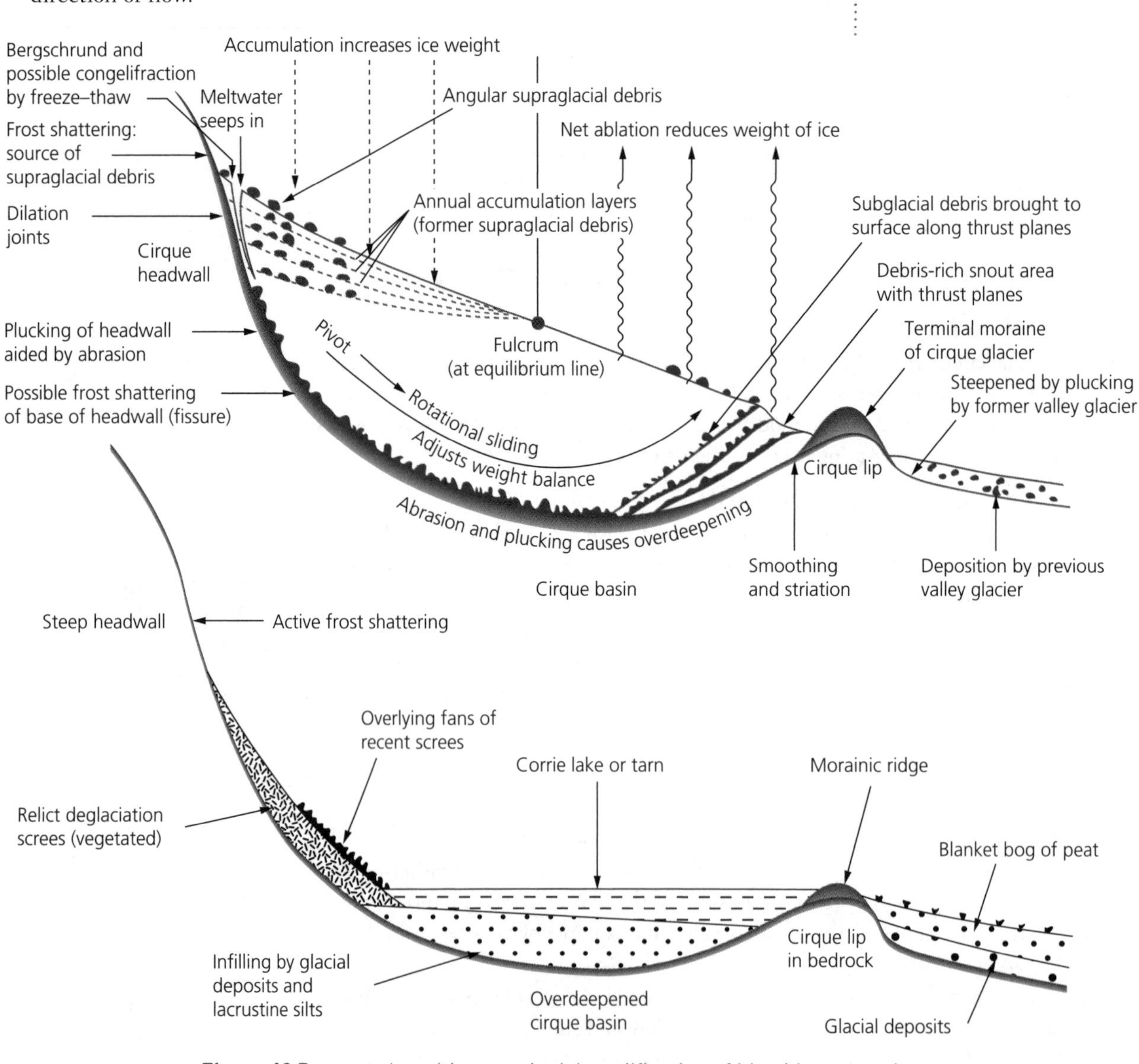

Figure 18 Present-day with post-glacial modification of Llyn Lluncaws cirque in the Berwyn Mountains in Wales

Summary

- Glacial processes, landforms and landscapes change over different timescales from seconds to millennia.
- Rapid mass movements, sometimes caused by volcanoes or earthquakes, can cause changes such as avalanches, lahars and glacial outburst floods.
- Seasonal (annual) changes occur, with the melting and freezing of water resulting in seasonal variations of fluvioglacial transport and deposition, including features such as varved deposits.
- Over millennia, glacial landscapes are reworked with infilling of glacial lakes and kettle holes and changes in drainage patterns.

Glacial processes are a vital context for human activity

Impacts of glacial processes and landforms on human activity

Current glacial processes can have a dramatic impact on human activities. This can be well illustrated by glacial lake outburst floods (GLOFs) as well as the loss of glacial meltwaters resulting from climate change.

Glacial lake outburst floods

A glacial lake outburst flood is also known by the Icelandic term **jökulhlaup**. It is a powerful flood caused by the sudden discharge of a subglacial or ice moraine-dammed lake. There is potential for an outburst flood whenever meltwater collects behind an ice or moraine obstruction. The sudden catastrophic release can be triggered in six main ways:

1. increased flotation of ice, as water levels rise
2. overflow and melting of an ice dam, common in climate warming
3. breakdown of an ice dam because of tectonic activity
4. irreversible overtopping of a moraine dam by large tsunami-style waves triggered by a snow or ice avalanche, or a landslide into a lake
5. failure of a moraine dam by slow melting of ice within it or removal of fine sediment from the moraine by underwater 'piping'
6. enlargement of pre-existing tunnels beneath an ice dam because of increased water pressure

Note that outburst floods may be cyclical in nature because the ice dam and lake may reform following a flood.

These large floods are a huge threat to people and property in inhabited mountain valleys around the world. They may destroy property situated tens or even hundreds of kilometres from their source, especially in areas with a long history of settlement, for example the Andes, European Alps and Himalayas.

Changes to the hydrological cycle resulting from climate warming

The impacts of climate warming on the hydrological cycle will have serious consequences for millions of people. In mountainous areas such as the Andes and Himalayas, glacial meltwater feeds rivers. 95% of Himalayan glaciers are in rapid retreat, and changes in discharge will have knock-on effects on sediment yield and water quality. For example, the Khumbu glacier, one of the highest in the world, has retreated more than 5 km since 1953.

Rivers in Asia, such as the Mekong, Yangtze, Brahmaputra, Ganges and Hwang He, are all fed by Himalayan glacial meltwater. The loss of a steady supply has huge implications for the two powerhouses of India and China (which together have more than one-third of the world's population) which are both emerging as superpowers with almost insatiable demands on water for development of their economies and the quality of life of their populations.

Western China's semi-desert area is home to 350 million farmers dependent on water supplied from the glaciers of the Tibetan plateau, an area experiencing high amounts of glacial thinning. Water shortages could affect 538 million people — some 42% of China's people — hence the development of massive hard engineering solutions for water security, such as dams and the South–North Water Transfer Project.

In India the reduction of glacial meltwater flowing into the Ganges–Brahmaputra system is likely to result in at least 500 million people facing water shortages, with nearly 40% of India's irrigated (post-Green Revolution) bread basket being affected.

Impacts of human activity on glacial processes and landforms

There are a number of ways in which humans affect glacial processes and landforms both directly, via exploitation of glacial resources, and indirectly, via large-scale anthropogenic climate change, which has had such a disastrous impact on the mass balance of up to 75% of the world's glaciers.

For example, the active Arctic glacier environment has been subjected to multiple stressors, not only from greenhouse gas emissions which lead to climate warming, but also from global pollution and the increasing impact of resource exploitation, such as oil production on the Alaska North Slope, as well as mining and tourism. Relict glacial environments, such as the Swiss Alps, are more economically exploited but are possibly less vulnerable to this exploitation.

Knowledge check 23

Explain why relict landscapes are less fragile and less vulnerable to exploitation.

Mining and quarrying

Glacial erosion plays an important role in removing regolith (loose overlying soil) and vegetation to expose economically valuable rocks. Many active and relict mountainous areas are composed of igneous and metamorphic rocks containing valuable mineral deposits and ores, which are mined, and rocks such as slate, which are quarried. In lowland areas, outwash deposits from the Pleistocene ice sheets provide an important source of materials for the building industry, pre-sorted by meltwater into sands and gravels to be sold as aggregates for making concrete, etc. These sand and gravel quarries are common in Jutland in western Denmark and in the Netherlands. In the UK, the building industry uses around 250 million tonnes of sand, gravel and aggregates each year. The sources reflect the geography of ice sheet deposition, with eskers, kames and outwash fans all supplying sand and gravels.

Hydroelectricity

Generation of hydroelectric power (HEP) is a major use of water derived from glaciers. Both Norway and New Zealand derive over 90% of their electricity from this source. Sometimes, meltwaters are used directly, although with recent climate change these flows are unpredictable. Occasionally water is diverted via tunnels from subglacial streams, for example in Mauranger in southwest Norway where water comes via a tunnel from the Bondhusbreen glacier. More usually, either a natural ribbon lake or a dam and reservoir in a glaciated valley provide the HEP. Switzerland has more than 500 HEP stations, producing some 70% of its electricity. HEP is a renewable 'green' source, although there are issues both with reliability of water supply and environmental concerns over damming of rivers. In mountain villages of developing nations such as Nepal or Bolivia, micro-hydros can revolutionise the quality of life.

Knowledge check 24

To what extent is hydroelectric power a 'green' source of energy?

Tourism

The tourism industry has seen tremendous growth in recent decades. This has brought many economic benefits to mountain regions, with visitors attracted to the spectacular scenery of both present-day and relict glaciated landscapes. In Alpine landscapes, a huge range of outdoor pursuits are possible — hill walking, climbing, mountaineering and skiing may allow whole regions to capitalise on their tourist potential with the exponential growth of year-round activities. In the Rockies, for instance, there are many multipurpose resorts such as Banff in Alberta, Aspen in Colorado and Whistler in British Columbia which form urban honeypot enclaves within glaciated environments.

Glaciated regions are increasingly visited for the glaciers themselves, which puts pressure on these fragile landscapes.

The **pleasure periphery** is the process by which long-haul travel and modern communications have brought mass tourism not only to traditional areas, such as the Swiss Alps and the Rockies, but also to remote polar regions in the Arctic (Alaska, Greenland, Iceland and Svalbard) and Antarctic (South Georgia and the Antarctic peninsula). These areas have become increasingly popular, especially for expedition ship cruising, which has many implications for their environments.

The economic value of mountain tourism requires careful management of the benefits so that these are not outweighed by environmental costs to the scenery and to the local culture. It is a fine balance! So much depends on the fragility of the landscape and the nature and intensity of the economic activities (see the case study on pp. 51–52).

Management of glaciated landscapes

There are a number of possible approaches to management of cold environments, as shown by Figure 19.

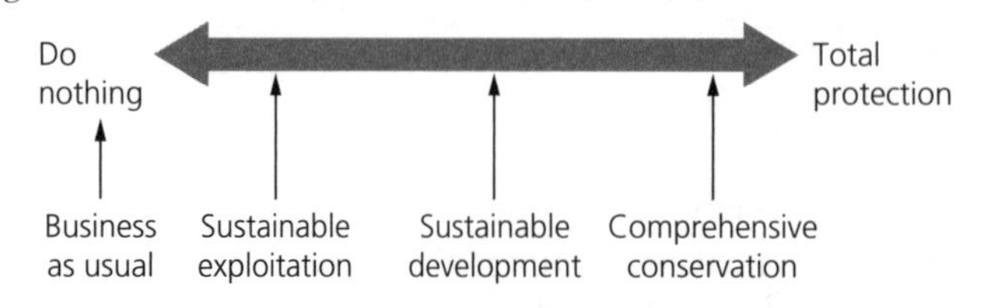

Figure 19 The spectrum of management for cold environments

- **Do nothing** lies at one end of the spectrum. It allows multiple economic uses to flourish. The ethos would be to allow cold environments to be exploited for whatever resources are in demand and are profitable. This approach might be supported by governments at local or national level for the revenues it brings, or by some local people, e.g. Chambers of Commerce or trades unions for employment potential, or by developers such as industrialists and globalised transnational corporations (TNCs), such as energy and mining companies.
- **Business as usual** is a similar approach to do nothing, leaving the area as it currently stands but possibly including aspects of pre-existing sustainability such as self-regulation on environmental issues. All TNCs have pre-existing Environmental Policies as part of their Mission Statements. By keeping the status quo, most players are content, except for the conservationists.
- **Sustainable exploitation** can be regarded as a middle way, as it targets development for profit but with the insistence on mandatory environmental regulation, for example of waste disposal. It can be channelled to provide distinctive benefits for the community, such as in the development of fishing for local communities or sustainable hunting. In theory it takes into account the vested interests of many players at a variety of scales, but it relies on considerable compromise to be successful.
- **Sustainable development** management attempts to develop an area in a way that uses resources for the benefit of the existing community without destroying the environment, but at the same time conserving resources for future generations. The four facets of the sustainability quadrant or the three facets of the stool of sustainability are difficult to achieve, especially in cold environments (see Figure 20).

  There are tensional forces between the need to conserve fragile vulnerable environments and at the same time to exploit vital resources for the economic wellbeing of future generations. This is clearly demonstrated by the controversy over Alaskan oil where there is a clash between environmentalists, local indigenous peoples, state and national governments, and oil companies. Many NGOs, such as the World Wide Fund for Nature (WWF), favour the approach of sustainable development as ultimately it could conserve the landscape and support indigenous communities.

Futurity	'Greenness'
Pro-poor	Bottom-up community involvement

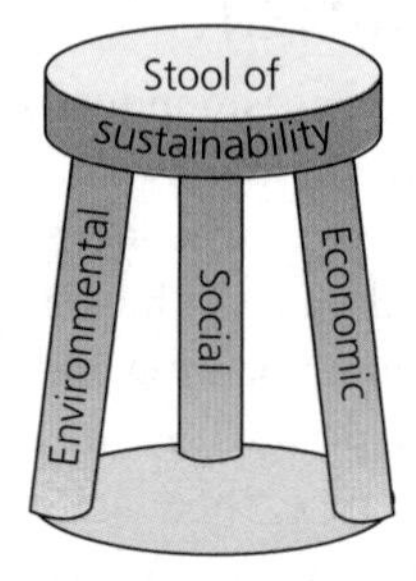

Figure 20 Assessing sustainability

Exam tip

Both the sustainability quadrant and the stool of sustainability are useful frameworks to support your work on management of glaciated areas.

Knowledge check 25

Explain three ways in which glaciated landscapes can be managed sustainably.

- **Comprehensive conservation** aims to protect and conserve glacial and periglacial environments as wilderness, especially where these are still in a pristine condition. The only exploitation allowed, such as carefully regulated ecotourism or organic eco-farming, is likely to be favoured by environmentalists and those allowed to practise and enjoy it — possibly local businesses and tourists. Exploitative activities, such as mining, would not be permitted. Governments might be ambivalent towards it as, in the short term, they may earn less income.
- **Total protection** is an approach favoured only by conservationists and some local traditionalists as it does not permit access to the pristine environment at all, except for scientific monitoring and research, and therefore does not allow local people to earn revenue from it or tourists to enjoy it.

Exam tip

The specification requires you to study context case studies. There are likely to be extended writing questions in the exam that invite you to use your case study.

Case study

The impact of human activity on the glacial landforms of the Alps

Hohe Tauern National Park, Austria

In 1995 the **Alpine Convention** was signed by eight European nations to promote sustainable development in designated areas in the Alps to protect the natural environment (largely a relict glaciated landscape) for future generations, yet at the same time promote socio-economic development to support the Alpine communities living within national parks. The eight protocols of the convention are designed to provide frameworks and guidelines for sustainable development, mountain farming, conservation of nature and landscape, protection of mountain forests, tourism, energy (HEP) generation, soil conservation and transport management.

Hohe Tauern National Park is one of seven national parks in Austria (see Figure 21) and the largest single protected area in the Alps. It is dominated by Grossglockner, a 3798 m high mountain, which is the source of several glaciers, including Pasterze, and contains many glaciated valleys, extensive Alpine tundra areas and several artificial lakes built for HEP generation.

The National Park is important for Alpine tourism, from extreme sports to glacier tourism, glacier skiing, climbing, walking and mountain biking. Globally, **mountain tourism** accounts for about 10% of annual tourism income; the ski industry generates around 5% of Austria's GDP and over 1 million people visit the National Park annually.

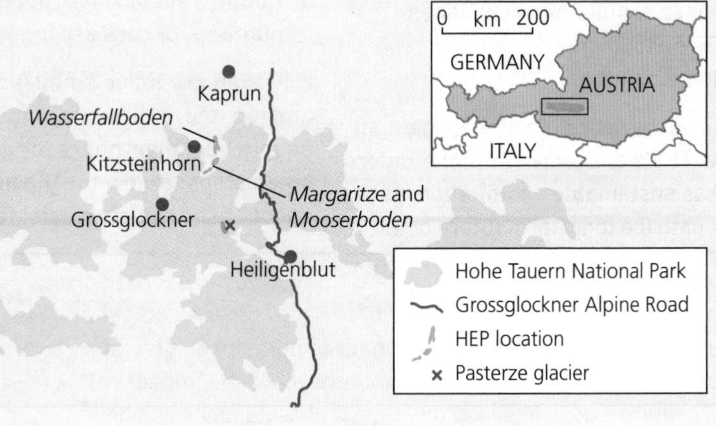

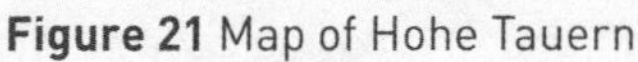
Figure 21 Map of Hohe Tauern

The environmental concerns about Alpine tourism include:

- the creation of ski pistes, which damage the fragile mountain ecosystems and lead to widespread felling of forests
- pollution from road users (largely air pollution), which has a major impact on the vegetation and air quality

The huge number of visitors, the fact that tourism is now all year round and the impacts of climate warming mean that problems are spreading to higher remote areas, as well as honeypots such as Zell am See. There is a need for careful management as tourism becomes potentially unsustainable.

The aims of the National Park are conflicting:

- encourage protection of the environment
- facilitate scientific research
- encourage tourism
- educate people about their environment

It is almost impossible to achieve a balance between promoting the use of the National Park and conserving its often fragile and frequently pristine environment. Tourism has been 'cited' as the main concern, as it has noticeably harmful impacts:

- erosion of pistes in the ski season — the damaged hillsides can be seen after the snow melts
- overuse of footpaths on popular walking routes, particularly near settlements
- use of snow cannons to generate artificial snow to lengthen the ski season, so delaying the spring snow melt with impacts on the spring flowers
- deforestation to allow the construction of ski pistes
- increasing numbers of buildings as villages expand outwards on to farmland
- air, water and noise pollution

Figure 19 (p. 50) shows the spectrum of management strategies available. The management of Hohe Tauern could be described as **sustainable exploitation**, as it attempts to ensure both the long-term future of the National Park and that the pristine landscape is not irreversibly damaged.

- Footpaths are well maintained (to avoid diversions and trampling into the most fragile tundra areas) and free hiking maps and signposting are provided. Some new routes in less well used and more robust areas have been developed.
- The park is administered in broad zones, with the core (high quality, relatively pristine area) having often limited access (permit only) and a peripheral area which is permanently settled and tourism encouraged.
- Numerous schemes are in place to support sustainable tourism and maintain farming, such as grants to support small family-run hotels, eco-hotels and agro tourism, with restaurants using local produce.
- As part of the Alpine Convention and network of Alpine protected areas, scientific research is carried out to find ways of protecting the natural environment.
- Certain villages have been designated sustainable tourist resorts, e.g. Heilingenblut and Neukirchen, both of which almost triple their population in the tourist season.
- In Neukirchen, the vulnerable sections of ski pistes are covered with snow to compact the route, and in summer the Alpine slopes are grazed by cows, which maintains the biodiversity and replenishes nutrients in the soil.
- Some ski lifts and many of the small hotels are powered by solar energy and the village uses its own local HEP.
- Public transport has been developed to reduce numbers of cars driving through the park.

However, are these small-scale measures too little and too late, especially in the glacier areas where people queue for hours for guided tours down the steep steps to view the glacier, or walk round the snout to see the proglacial features?

Exam tip

You have a choice of case study — either the impact of humans on glacial areas (e.g. Svalbard, Arctic Norway or Antarctic tourism) or the impacts of glacial landforms on human activities (e.g. the impact of avalanches and how they are managed). Geofact Sheet and Geofile both provide case studies.

Permafrost degradation through human activity

Traditionally, periglacial environments have been occupied by indigenous peoples, such as the Inuit in northern Canada, Greenland and Alaska, or the Sami in Lapland. They adapted their culture and lifestyles in remarkable ways to cope with harsh environments and live in symbiosis with the environments' fragility and vulnerability.

However, the establishment of permanent settlements and development of activities such as iron ore mining, oil extraction or military use require major technological advances to be successful, as permafrost creates a unique set of problems for construction work. Conventional construction techniques do not work because they alter the thermal balance of the ground, leading to permafrost thaw and widespread **ground subsidence**.

Landforms that develop on permafrost are dependent on the **heat energy exchange balance** between the atmosphere and the ground (Figure 22). The permafrost layer is sensitive to changes in this balance, because the seasonally active layer in which many of the periglacial processes work (frost heaving, ice lens development etc.) deepens rapidly with additional heat inputs from anthropogenic (human) activities.

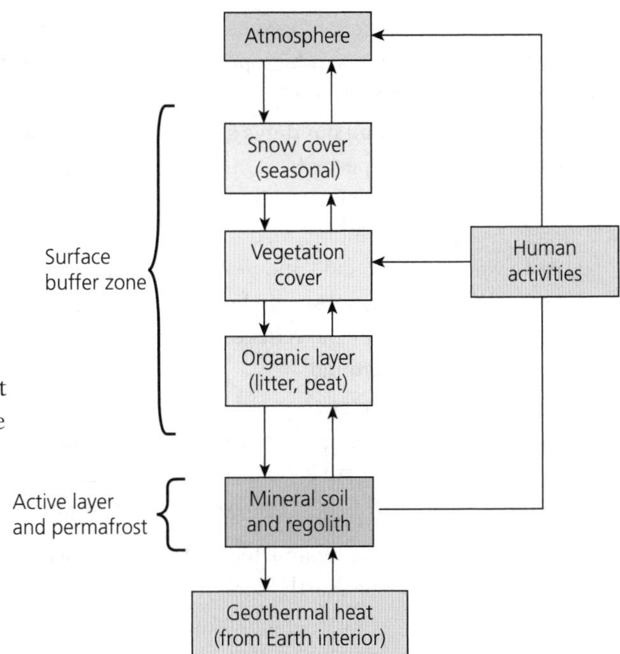

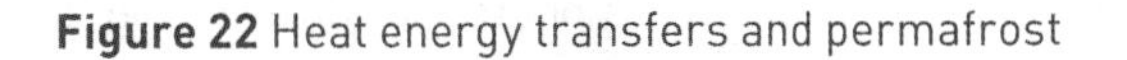
Figure 22 Heat energy transfers and permafrost

How the air–ground heat exchange works depends on the nature of the surface store. This consists of tundra vegetation cover, the organic surface layer of litter and peat, and the snow cover. The ability of this **energy exchange buffer zone** to store and transmit the heat energy controls the behaviour of the active and permafrost layers.

Problems occur when the tundra vegetation, or even the snow cover, is cleared from the surface, for example to keep an airport open. This reduces insulation of the permafrost so deepening the active layer in summer as heat is transferred down to the permafrost 'table' more easily. At Inuvik in northern Canada development increased the depth of the active layer from 30 cm to 183 cm in eight years, following deforestation. In Central Alaska the permafrost layer melted rapidly after vegetation clearance, causing ground disturbance and releasing carbon from peat stores. Even minor disturbances of vegetation cover, for example by off-road vehicles used by mining companies, can greatly increase melting of the ground ice over the long term.

Ground subsidence is especially prevalent where the upper layer of the permafrost is ice rich, close to rivers or in fine-grained sediments with high porosity and much interstitial ice, as the deepening of the active layer causes a larger volume of ground ice to melt relative to the original frozen volume of the sediment.

Large buildings or structures such as the Trans-Alaska pipeline transmit large quantities of additional heat to the ground, so exacerbating the effect of reduced insulation of the permafrost layer.

The damage caused by this form of ground subsidence can be seen all over Siberia, northern Canada and Alaska, as infrastructure such as roads, railways, bridges and airstrips is severely damaged, thus requiring constant maintenance.

New methods of construction have been developed to successfully offset the problems, but these come at a high price, adding to the cost of exploitation of resources or building settlements.

- Houses and other small buildings are often raised about 1 m above the ground on pipes driven into the permafrost, allowing air to circulate and remove heat that would otherwise be conducted into the ground.
- Larger structures, including roads, bridges and airstrips, are built on **aggregate pads** (layers of coarse sand and gravel, typically 1.5 m thick). They provide a substitute for the insulating effect of the vegetation and reduce transfer of heat from the buildings to the ground.
- Utilities such as water, energy and waste disposal present a further challenge, hence the use of **utilidors** (see Figure 23). These are economic only for larger settlements such as Inuvit or Longyearbyen in Svalbard.

The Trans-Alaska pipeline, completed in 1977 to transport oil across Alaska from the North Slope to Valdez in southern Alaska and hence to mainland USA, is an interesting example of how technology was used, to combat not only the impact of ground subsidence of the permafrost but also environmental damage to a pristine environment.

Exam tip

Read through the section on periglacial processes and landforms to familiarise yourself with the key terms in order to understand the degradation caused by human activity.

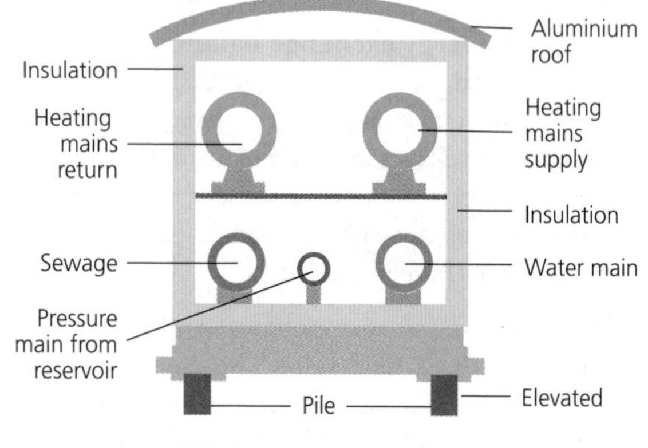

Figure 23 Utilidors and how they work

Summary

- Glacial processes and landforms impact human activity, for example glacial outburst floods.
- Human activity impacts glacial processes and landforms, such as degradation of highland glaciated landscapes through tourism, the extraction of glacially deposited sands and gravels and the creation of reservoirs for HEP.
- You will need to know one case study of one management strategy to manage either the impacts of glacial processes/landforms on human activity, or human activity impacts on glacial processes/landforms.
- Modern human activity, such as permanent settlement, mining and oil extraction degrade permafrost and require technical solutions to solve problems of melting, ground subsidence and carbon release.

Tectonic hazards

Tectonic processes and hazards

The structure of the Earth

The Earth's structure has been analysed by scientists studying patterns of shockwaves (caused by earthquakes). They have identified a number of layers, with different densities, chemical composition and physical properties (see Figure 24).

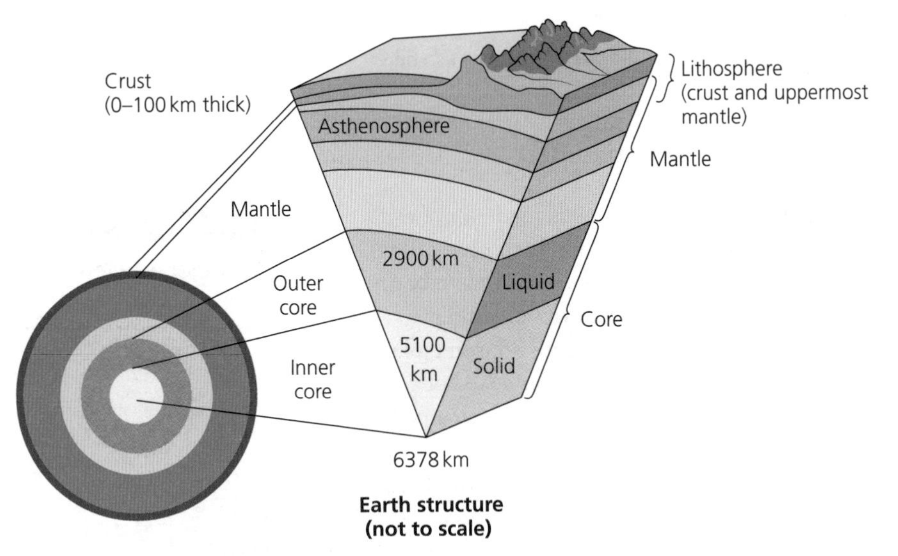

Figure 24 The structure of the Earth

The Earth can be divided into three layers: the core, the mantle and the crust, based on its density and chemical composition.

- The **core** consists of iron and nickel and is about the size of the planet Mars. The outer core is in a semi-molten state but the inner core is solid. The temperature at the centre of the Earth (6378 km below the Earth's surface) is about 6200°C (even hotter than the surface of the sun).
- The **mantle** is composed mainly of silicate rocks, rich in iron and magnesium. Apart from the solid top layer (known as the **asthenosphere**) the rocks in the mantle are in a semi-molten state. The mantle extends to a depth of 2900 km where temperatures may exceed 5000°C. It is this high temperature that generates **convection currents**, which were identified as a mechanism driving plate movements.
- In relative terms, the **crust** is as thin as the skin of an apple is to its flesh. The crust is divided into:
  - **a** **oceanic crust** (known as **sima** as it is composed predominantly of **si**lica and **ma**gnesium), a layer consisting mainly of basalt. It averages 6–10 km in thickness; at its deepest point it has a temperature of 1200°C
  - **b** **continental crust** (**sial**, so called as it is composed of **si**lica and **al**umina), can be up to 70 km thick, and is composed largely of granite

Table 7 summarises the difference between the two types of crust.

Table 7 Differences between the two types of crust

	Oceanic crust	Continental crust
Maximum age	180 million years	3.5 billion years
Thickness (km)	6–10	25–75
Area of Earth's surface	60%	40%
Density ($g\,cm^{-3}$)	3.3	2.7
Rock type	Basaltic	Granitic

The crust is separated from the mantle by the **Moho discontinuity** (named after Mohorovičić, the Croatian scientist who first discovered it).

The crust and the rigid top layers of the mantle are collectively known as the **lithosphere**.

Knowledge check 26

In which layer of the Earth's structure is the asthenosphere found?

The mechanics of plate tectonics

The theory of plate tectonics states that the Earth's surface is made up of rigid lithospheric plates (seven major, seven smaller minor, and many more small plates known as micro-plates). There are some areas where the pattern of plate boundaries is so complex, such as Iran and Indonesia, that they appear rather similar to the smashed shells of hard boiled eggs. As can be seen from Figure 25, some plates contain largely continental crust (Eurasian plate), others are composed of continental and oceanic crust, whereas yet others contain only oceanic crust (Nazca plate).

Knowledge check 27

Name the seven major plates.

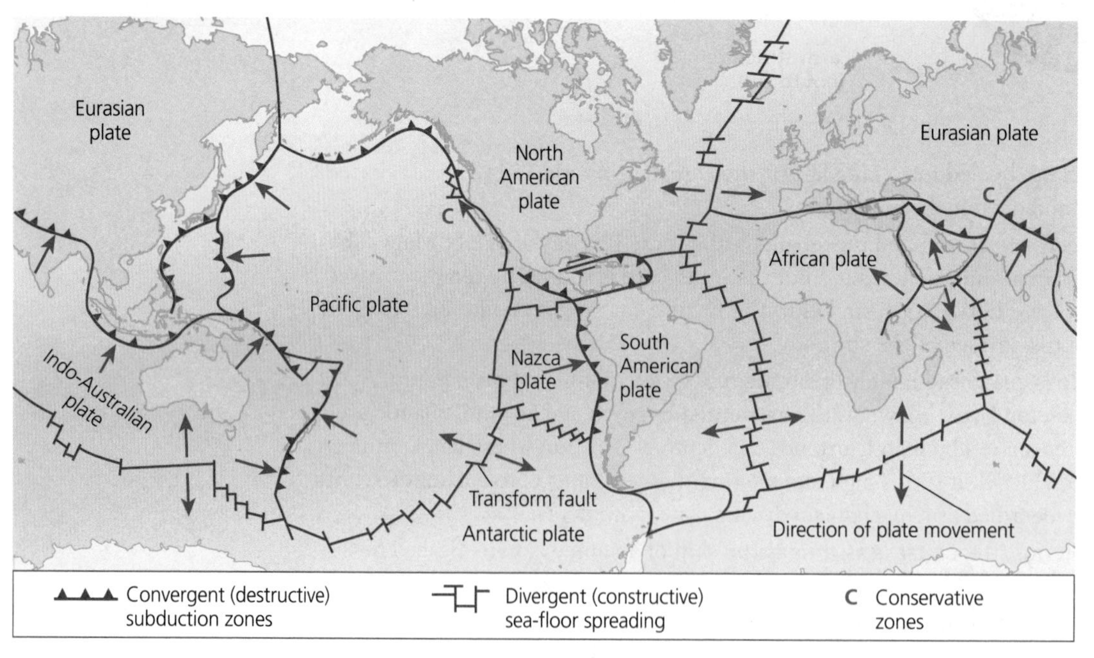

Figure 25 The main tectonic plates

The original idea was that the rising limbs of convection cells (at the spreading ridge) move heat from the Earth's core towards the surface, spreading out either side of the ridge and carrying the plates with it. The plates 'float' on a lubricated layer between the upper mantle and the lithosphere — the asthenosphere. This lubricated layer allows the solid lithosphere to move over the upper mantle (Figure 26).

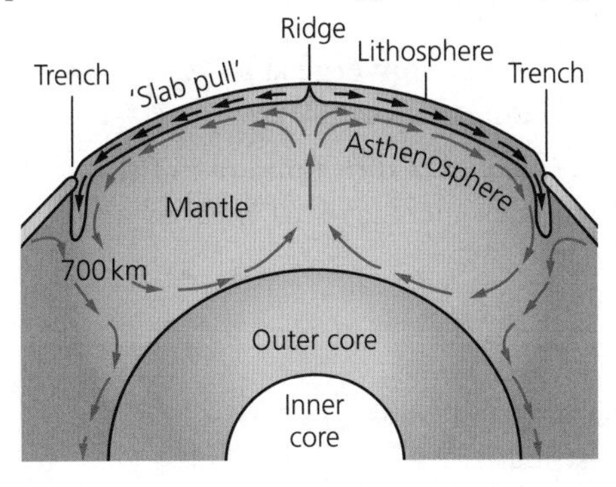

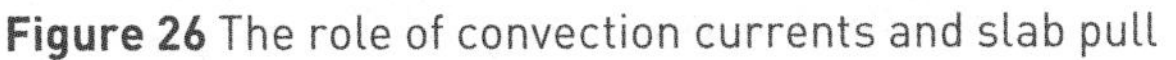

Figure 26 The role of convection currents and slab pull

Modern thinking on plate movement

Modern imaging techniques (tomography) have been unable to identify convection cells in the mantle that are sufficiently large to drive plate movement, so the idea of the asthenosphere as a 'conveyor' of plates has been modified. It has also been discovered that the injection of fresh magma associated with sea floor spreading at the ocean ridges does not **push** the plates apart, instead it is more of a passive process — a case of filling a gap rather than forcibly injecting material into the lithosphere.

Molten material wells up at divergent plate boundaries because of thinning of the lithosphere, and the consequent decrease in pressure causes partial melting of the upper mantle. As the lithosphere is heated, it rises and becomes elevated above the surrounding sea floor to form an ocean ridge. This elevation produces a slope down and away from the ridge. Fresh rock formed at the spreading centres is relatively hot, less dense and more buoyant than rock further away from the divergent margin, which becomes increasingly older, cooler and denser.

Gravity acts on this older, denser lithosphere causing it to slide away from the spreading ridge. As a result, the lithosphere is thinned at the ridge, creating yet more partial melting and upwelling of magma. This process, known as **ridge push**, was initially identified as the key driver of movement but it is now considered to be a passive process — it is the **gravitational sliding** that is now considered to be the active force driving plate movement. It is the density differences across the plates that are of key importance. **Slab pull** occurs at subduction zones where the colder, denser portions of the plates sink into the mantle and this **pulls** the remainder of the plates along. Therefore it is **slab pull** that is the key mechanism for plate movement.

Evidence from tomography (seismic scans) supports this theory as the cold dense slabs of plate deep in the Earth's mantle have been identified.

The development of plate tectonics as a theory evolved over many years from a concept to a credible mechanism, but it remains just a theory because the cost of drilling down for proof is prohibitively expensive and impractical. The mechanism by which tectonic plates move is highly complex and remains a subject of debate.

Exam tip

As plate tectonics is a theory it cannot be proven. Ideas on plate movement mechanisms will develop, so keep up to date. For examples see the USGS website.

Exam tip

When answering questions on plate tectonics do not include the story of continental drift in your answer.

Plate movements

Plates move slowly and irregularly in relation to each other, typically at rates of 4 cm per year. Three types of movement are recognised.

1 In some locations plates move away from each other, i.e. they **diverge** at a **constructive margin**, e.g. East African Rift Valley.
2 In other locations plates move towards each other, i.e. they **converge** at a **destructive** margin, for example off the coast of South America.
3 In a few places plates move past each other, either in opposite directions, or in the same direction at different speeds, i.e. a **transform** movement, at what is called a conservative margin.

Plate tectonic settings

Table 8 summarises the main settings, processes, hazards and landforms. These settings are fundamental in explaining the spatial distribution and occurrence of nearly all tectonic hazards and landforms (see p. 65 for exceptions).

Table 8 Tectonic settings

Tectonic setting	Motion (processes)	Hazards	Example	Landforms
Constructive plate boundaries (divergent margin)	Two oceanic plates moving apart	Basaltic volcanoes and minor, shallow earthquakes	Mid-Atlantic ridge (Iceland), mostly submerged	Lava plateaux Ocean ridge features
	Two continental plates moving apart	Basaltic spatter cones and minor earthquakes	Mt Nyiragongo (DRC) in the East African Rift Valley	Rift valley landscapes
Destructive plate boundaries (convergent margin)	Two oceanic plates in collision	Island arc explosive andesitic eruptions and earthquakes	Soufrière Hills on Montserrat, Aleutian Islands	Island arcs of volcanoes
	Two continental plates in collision	Major, shallow earthquakes, long thrust faults	Himalayan orogenic belt collision zone	Compressional mountain belts
	Oceanic and continental plates in collision	Explosive, andesitic eruptions and major earthquakes	Andes mountain chain and volcanoes	Complex mountain landscapes with fold mountains and volcanoes
Transform boundaries (conservative margin)	Plates sliding past one another	Major shallow earthquakes No volcanic activity	San Andreas fault, California, North Anatolian fault, Haiti	Strike-slip faulted landscapes
Hotspots	Oceanic	Basaltic shield volcanoes and minor earthquakes	Hawaiian island chains, Galapagos Islands	Volcanic landscapes
	Continental	Colossal rhyolitic mega-eruptions	Yellowstone 'supervolcano', USA	'Roots' of super volcanoes

Exam tip

Table 8 is a useful summary. Make sure you learn it.

Knowledge check 28

Which tectonic settings have (a) the most violent earthquakes, (b) the most explosive volcanic eruptions?

Constructive plate margins

Two plates of oceanic crust

The movement of the plates apart is due to the divergence driven by **slab pull**, which brings magma from the asthenosphere to the surface. The pressure from the margins leads to a doming up of the Earth's surface and the formation of a ridge such as the mid-Atlantic ridge (Figure 27). This ridge and rift system extends along the mid-Atlantic for about 10,000 km. It was created about 60 million years ago when Greenland (on the North American plate) and northwest Scotland (on the Eurasian plate) separated to form the Atlantic Ocean. The **average** rate of movement is 0.025 m per year. There is a series of underwater volcanoes along the margin, which occasionally form a volcanic island. Iceland is one such volcanic island, much of which formed from a lava plateau about 200 m above sea level, as basic lava poured out through numerous tensional faults (fissures) formed by a hotspot plume. Subsidence of sections of crust between fault lines formed the rift valley, clearly visible at Thingvellir, and there are also active volcanoes such as Hekla and Grimsvotn linked to individual vents from the hotspots.

Most of the earthquake activity at a constructive margin is shallow, low magnitude and high frequency, often along transform faults as the mid-ocean ridge is offset. In June 2000 a significant earthquake, MM scale 6.5, occurred on the south coast of Iceland.

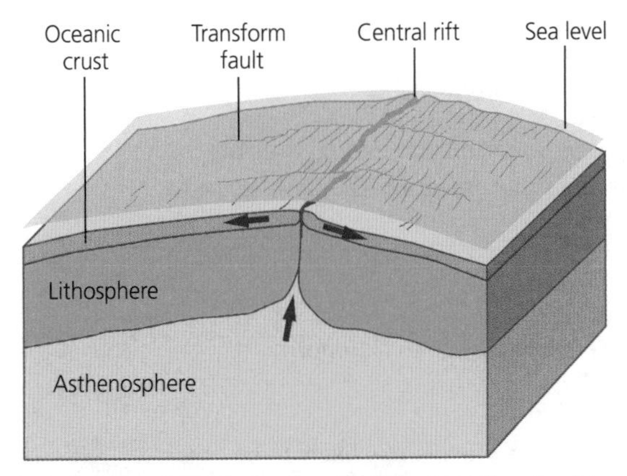

Figure 27 A cross-section of the mid-Atlantic ridge

Two plates of continental crust

The East African Rift Valley is an example of a constructive margin in an area of continental crust. Eastern Africa is moving in a northeasterly direction, diverging from the main African plate, which is 'heading' north. The rift valley, which consists of two broadly parallel branches, extends for 4000 km from Mozambique to the Red Sea. Inward-facing fault line scarps (eroded fault scarps) reach heights more than 600 m above the valley floor.

Knowledge check 29

Explain the difference between a fault scarp and a fault line scarp.

Figure 28 shows the following features.

- Linear mountain ranges (ridges) form as a result of the buoyancy of hot, low-density margins, which forces the crust to bulge upwards along the plate margins.
- A central rift in the ridge forms because of subsidence between normal faults to form a rift valley.
- Chains of lakes (e.g. Lake Tanganyika) form in the basins as the rift opens up.
- Fissure eruptions occur from a series of basaltic lava flows.
- Some large volcanoes (e.g. Kilimanjaro) form where the crust has thinned by tension and rising magma is extruded through the weaknesses.
- Numerous small basaltic cinder cones form on the rift valley floor, often made of lava and some ash (composite).
- Minor igneous intrusions occur, flowing up through the faults and fissures to form dykes.

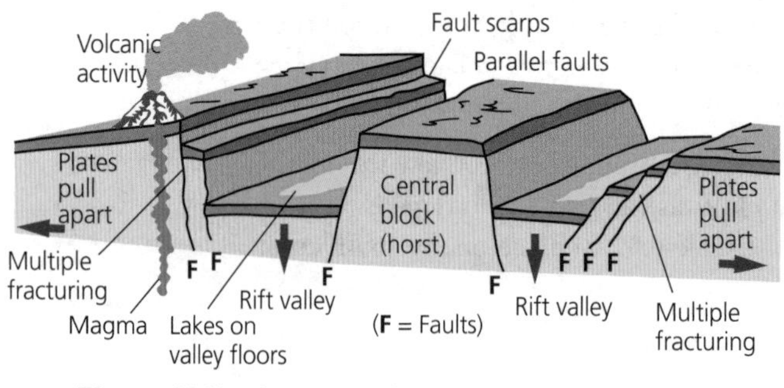

Figure 28 Key features of the rift valley landscape

Over time the rift valley is reshaped, for example by waterfalls cascading over the lava plateau and by present-day weathering and mass movement on the fault scarp to create fault line scarps.

Destructive plate margins

Destructive plate margins occur when two plates converge due to slab pull.

Ocean crust to ocean crust

When two oceanic plates converge, subduction occurs, as one plate is likely to be slightly older, colder or denser than the other. This plate is **subducted**, heated and eventually melts under pressure at around 100 km below the surface. The melted material rises up through any lines of weakness towards the surface. Extrusive volcanic activity results in the formation of a chain of volcanic islands above the subduction zone, known as **an island arc**. As Figure 29 shows, the Mariana Islands have been formed in this way through the convergence of the Pacific plate and the Philippine plate, with the Pacific plate being subducted to form the deep Marianas Trench. Earthquakes of high magnitude are focused along the subducted plate (the **Benioff zone**).

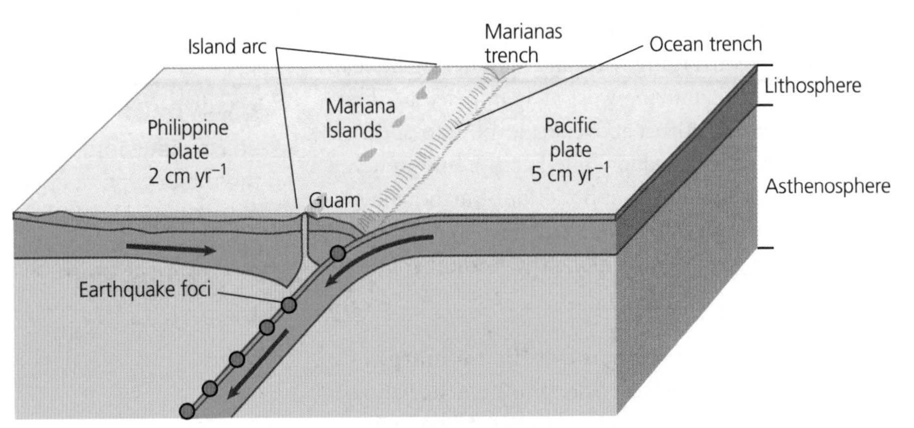

Figure 29 Cross-section of an oceanic/oceanic destructive margin

Oceanic to continental

Oceanic crust is denser than continental crust, so where these two types of crust converge, the more dense crust is subducted down into the asthenosphere by slab pull. Again, an ocean trench is formed on the sea floor at the point of **subduction**. The continental crust, because it is lighter and more buoyant, is not subducted but is uplifted and buckled, faulted and folded to form a range of mountains (Figure 30). Rising magma again breaks through any lines of weakness to form volcanoes, with infrequent but violent eruptions, or may solidify beneath the surface, forming intrusive igneous rocks such as granite batholiths which can be subsequently exposed by numerous years of erosion.

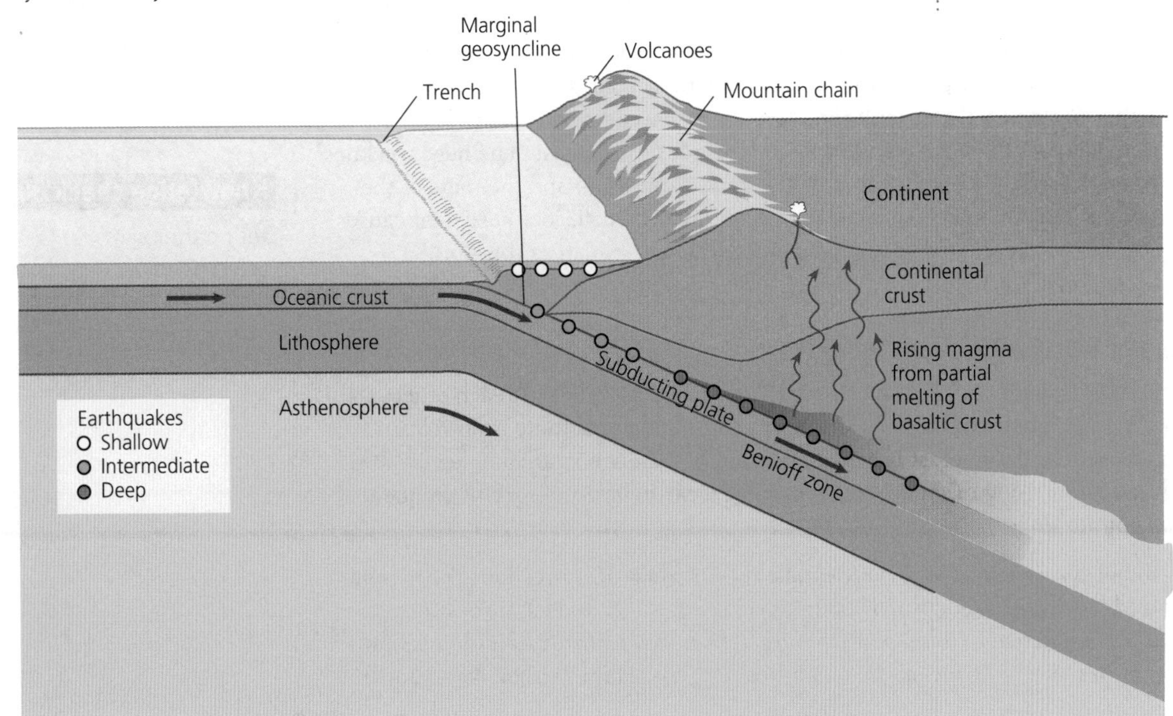

Figure 30 Cross-section of oceanic/continental destructive margin

An example is found in South America, where the oceanic Nazca plate is moving east at approximately 12 cm per year and is converging with and subducting beneath the continental South American plate, which is moving west at 1 cm per year. The Andes, a chain of fold mountains, rises nearly 7000 m above sea level, interspersed with many active volcanoes such as Cotopaxi in Ecuador. The Peru–Chile trench, which reaches depths of 8000 m, occurs at the point of subduction. Earthquakes (e.g. in northern Peru in 1970 and in Ecuador in 2016) are frequent and often of huge magnitude (up to MM 9) and occur at a range of depths along the Benioff zone.

Exam tip

Learn diagrams of all the major types of plate movement. Use full annotations.

Continental to continental: collision margins

Where two plates of continental crust converge is known as a **collision margin**. As the plates are both buoyant and composed of lower density granite material, no subduction occurs. However, former ocean sediments trapped between the two converging plates are heaved upward, under intense compression (formation of **thrust faults** and nappes), resulting in the formation of major complex mountain belts. Usually no volcanic activity is found at this type of margin as no crust is being destroyed by subduction and no new crust is being created by rising magma. However, earthquakes do occur. Some are of deeper focus and therefore have less surface impact, but shallow, highly hazardous earthquakes also occur, often in populated foothill areas as in Nepal.

A good example of a collision zone is the Himalayas. The Indo-Australian plate is moving northwards at a rate of about 5–6 cm per year, so colliding with the Eurasian plate. Prior to their collision, the two continental landmasses were separated by the remnants of the Tethys Sea, which originated when Pangaea broke up around 300 million years ago.

As the two plates collided, the Himalayas were formed (orogenesis). These mountain belts are geologically complex as the intense compression caused not only extreme folds (nappes), but also thrust faults and accretionary wedging on uplift. The mountain belt rises to heights of 9000 m and includes Mt Everest. The huge thickness of sediment forced the crust downwards (isostatic depression) and the roots of the mountain belt are found deep in the Earth's interior. The collision movement causes great stresses which are released by periodic earthquakes, such as the Gorkha earthquake in Nepal, 2015.

Knowledge check 30

Define the term 'orogenesis'.

Conservative plate margins

A conservative margin is found where two plates move laterally past each other — this is known as a **transform movement**. As at collision margins there is no volcanic activity here because no crust is being destroyed by subduction and no new crust is being created by rising magma. However, shallow earthquakes of varying frequency and magnitude do occur.

High frequency, low magnitude earthquakes occur when pressure along the margin is relatively easily released, usually up to ten every day. Occasional major events take place after a significant build-up of pressure, typically when high levels of friction restrict movement along the original fault lines (e.g. the Haiti earthquake of 2010).

The best-known example of a conservative margin occurs in California at the San Andreas fault, where the Pacific plate and North American plate meet. The Pacific plate is moving northwestwards at a rate of 6 cm per year, while the North American plate, although moving in the same general direction, is only moving at about 1 cm per year. While earth tremors are very common, the 'Big One', such as occurred at San Francisco in 1906 and 1989, occurs only rarely.

Figure 31 summarises the main features found at a conservative margin, largely associated with erosion along the fault line.

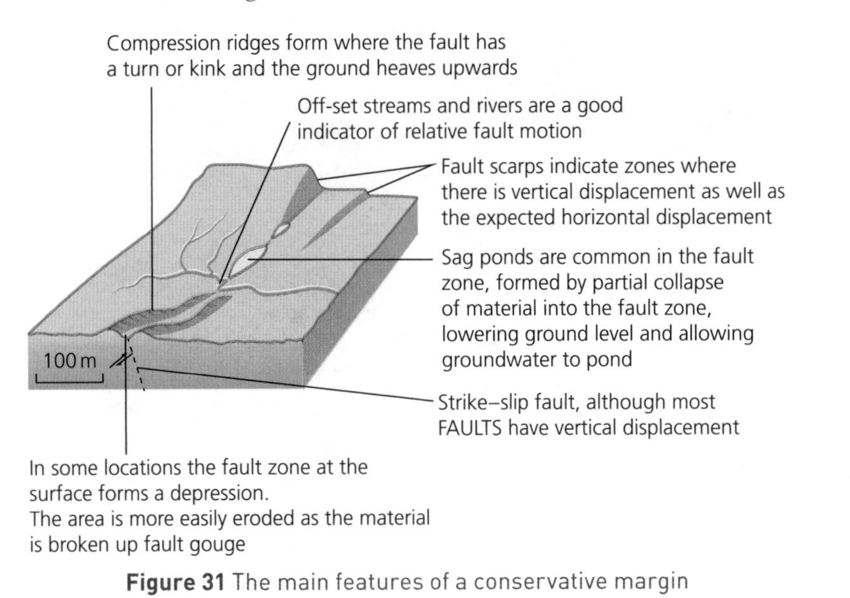

Figure 31 The main features of a conservative margin

Hotspots

Hotspots are small areas of the crust with an unusually high heat flow and are found away from plate boundaries.

Oceanic hotspots occur where plumes of magma are rising from the asthenosphere. If the crust is particularly thin or weak, magma may escape on to the surface as a volcanic eruption. Lava may build up over time until it is above the present-day sea level, giving rise to volcanic islands.

The Hawaiian islands are a chain of volcanic islands (Figure 32) lying over a stable hotspot. The Pacific plate has been moving over the hotspot for about 70 million years, forming a succession of volcanic islands. As the plate has moved, so the volcanoes have been carried away from the hotspot in a northwesterly direction, forming a chain of extinct underwater volcanoes, called **sea mounts**, extending all the way towards the Aleutian Islands. Currently a new volcano, called Loihi, is erupting 35 km southeast of Big Island (Hawaii). It is only 3000 m tall and has risen only to 2000 m below sea level to date — it is estimated to reach the sea surface in 10,000–100,000 years' time. Big Island (Hawaii) volcanoes are extremely active — with frequent effusive eruptions from Kilauea. The high peaks Mauna Kea and Mauna Loa are actually higher than Mt Everest, but they start from well below sea level.

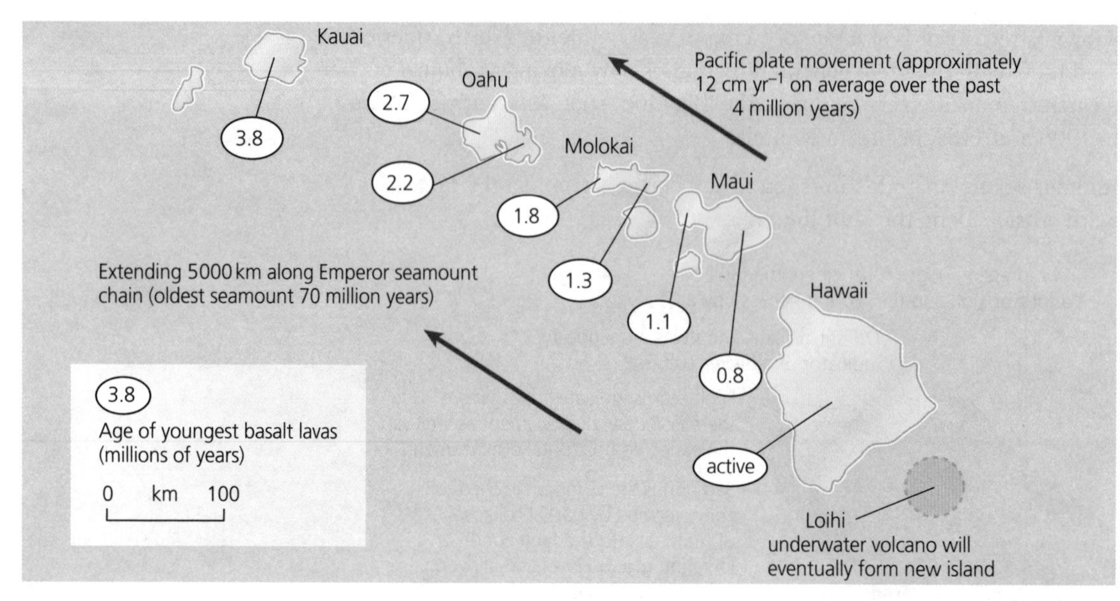

Figure 32 The Hawaiian hotspot

An example of a **continental hotspot** is found beneath Yellowstone National Park. The key feature is the probable explosive eruption of a rhyolitic super volcano, at the maximum of the VEI scale (see p. 69). Geological records suggest the Yellowstone event occurred 2.1 million years ago, ejecting 6000 times more gas and molten rock into the atmosphere than did the Mt St Helens eruption.

Global distribution of tectonic hazards

Primary tectonic hazards include earthquakes and volcanoes.

Earthquakes

Figure 33 shows the distribution of 30,000 earthquakes recorded over the last decade. The figure shows that the main zones of earthquakes are *not* randomly distributed but closely follow the plate boundaries.

The zones of earthquakes or **seismic** activity can be divided into four plate settings.

1 **Constructive** boundaries along the ocean ridges. Earthquakes in this zone are mainly shallow, and result from tensional transform faults in the crust and from shaking during volcanic activity. Along the oceanic ridges many earthquakes are submarine and pose little risk to people.

2 **Destructive** boundaries where oceanic crust is being subducted into the mantle beneath a continental plate, or where two oceanic plates collide in island arc zones. These areas are subject to frequent earthquakes, including high magnitude ones, and represent areas of major hazard. Tsunamis are most commonly generated by these earthquakes (e.g. 2004 Boxing Day tsunami).

3 **Destructive** boundaries where continental crust is colliding to produce fold mountain belts, e.g. the Alpine–Himalayan chain. Shallow earthquakes occur in a relatively broad zone, resulting in a high hazard risk (e.g. 1990 Bam earthquake in Iran) with the occasional deep-seated earthquake.

Exam tip

Re-read Table 8 **Tectonic settings** on p. 58 to piece together the key facts regarding the distribution of earthquakes and volcanoes, summarised here.

4 Areas of lateral crust movement (**transform**) in the continental regions produce mainly shallow earthquakes of high magnitude, such as at the conservative margin of the San Andreas fault system in California.

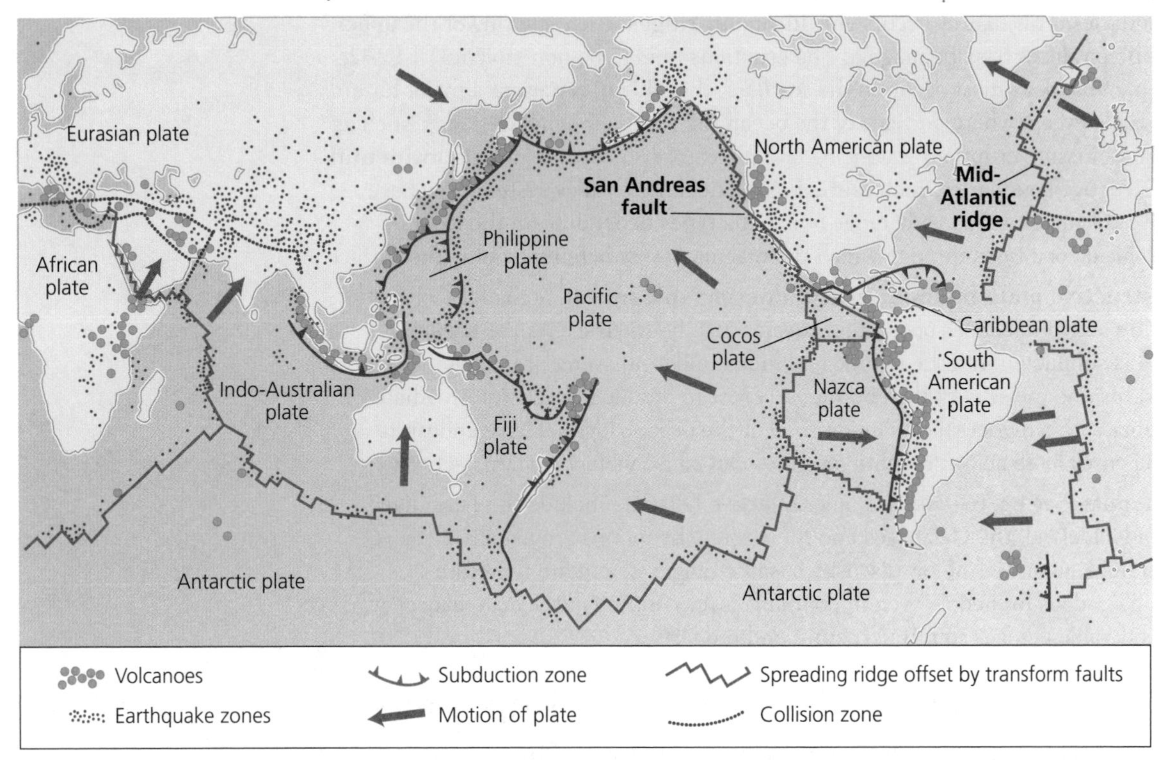

Figure 33 The global distribution of earthquakes and volcanoes

Additionally **intra-plate** earthquakes occur — some 15% of all earthquakes occur in relatively stable continental crust, away from plate boundaries. These earthquakes are caused by stresses created in crustal rocks, usually by movement along ancient fault lines (e.g. New Madrid in Missouri, USA, 1811/1812 and Tangshen in China, 1976, which resulted in 240,000 deaths), a process known as **isostatic recoil**. These intra-plate earthquakes are more dangerous because they are extremely unpredictable.

Quasi-natural earthquakes are those generated by human activity. It is thought that a 1993 earthquake in Killari, India, possibly resulted from the weight of water in a newly built reservoir behind a dam causing increased water pressure in the rock pores, which lubricated a fault line.

A recent controversial generator of earthquakes is **fracking** for unconventional supplies of oil and gas, which has led to numerous earthquakes in Oklahoma, and also in north Lancashire in the UK where fracking exploration was halted in 2015 as a result.

Exam tip

Always support your arguments with brief locational fact files of examples.

Knowledge check 31

Explain why fracking can lead to earthquakes.

Volcanoes

The chemical composition of lava depends on the geological situation in which it has formed. Basaltic (basic) lavas are formed by the melting of oceanic crust, whereas rhyolitic (acidic) lavas with a high silica content are formed from the melting of continental crust. Between these extremes are several groups of intermediate magmas, such as andesitic magma.

Knowledge check 32

Explain the difference between magma and lava.

The world's active volcanoes are found in three tectonic situations (see Figure 33).

1 **Constructive plate boundaries (rift volcanoes)**. Most of the magma that reaches the Earth's surface (around 75% in quantity) is extruded along these boundaries. This mainly occurs at **mid-ocean ridges** where melting of the upper mantle produces basaltic magma. The eruptions tend to be non-violent (VEI 1–2, see p. 69) and, as most occur on the sea floor, they do not represent a major hazard to people except where portions of the ocean ridge cross inhabited islands, such as Iceland. Fissure eruptions producing lava plateaux also occur widely. **Continental** constructive boundaries, such as the East African Rift Valley system, also have active volcanoes with a wide range of magma types depending on the local geological conditions through which the magma passes before reaching the surface.
2 **Destructive plate boundaries (subduction volcanoes)**. Some 80% of the world's active volcanoes occur along destructive boundaries. As the oceanic plate is subducted into the mantle and melts under pressure, basic magma rises upwards and mixes with the continental crust to produce largely intermediate magma with a higher silica content than at the ocean ridges. These andesitic, in some cases more acidic, rhyolitic magmas can cause violent volcanic activity.
3 **Hotspots**. See pp. 63–64. Examples of active hotspots include the Hawaiian Islands, Iceland, the Galapagos and the Azores. Eruptions are usually effusive with huge quantities of low viscosity basaltic magmas, and are therefore less hazardous for people even in populated areas, although they can cause considerable damage to infrastructure and property.

Physical hazard profiles and their impacts

Figure 34 compares the three major tectonic hazards in terms of their physical profiles. This is a qualitative technique that can be used to visually compare major hazard types, but also to look at a range of earthquakes or a series of volcanic eruptions.

Magnitude of earthquakes

Magnitude is considered to be the most important influence on the severity of impact of a tectonic hazard event. Magnitude is a quantifiable variable, especially for earthquakes. It can be defined as the size or physical force of a hazard event.

Earthquake magnitude is now measured by the logarithmic Moment Magnitude (MM) scale, a modification of the earlier **Richter scale**. The Richter scale was based on the amplitude of lines made on a seismogram, using the largest wave amplitude recorded. So the bigger the earthquake, the greater the earth shaking. For example, a 1-unit increase on the scale represents a ten times larger amplitude, i.e. it is a **logarithmic scale**. The MM scale is based on a number of parameters of an earthquake event, including the area of fault rupture and the amount of fault movement involved, which determines the amount of energy released. Results are similar to the Richter scale which is still widely used.

The **Mercalli scale** is also used to measure earthquakes. It is a descriptive scale that measures the amount of damage caused by surface shaking of particular earthquakes (see Table 9). Table 10 shows the relationship between earthquake magnitude and number of deaths resulting in a sample decade.

Exam tip

Use the MM scale, now widely used, as it is an improved version of the Richter scale.

Exam tip

Try to learn simple tables of dates, locations, magnitude and impacts of tectonic events.

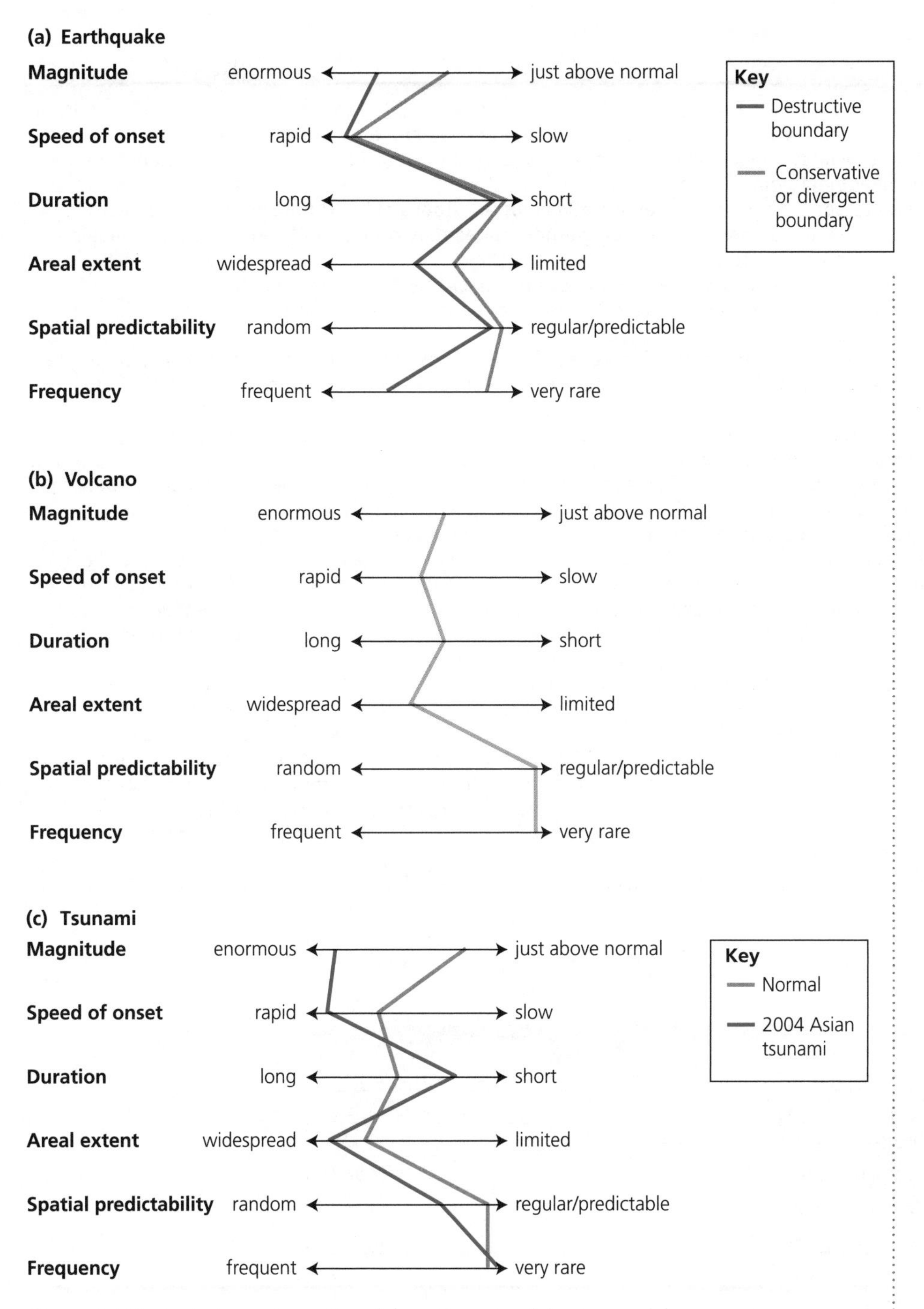

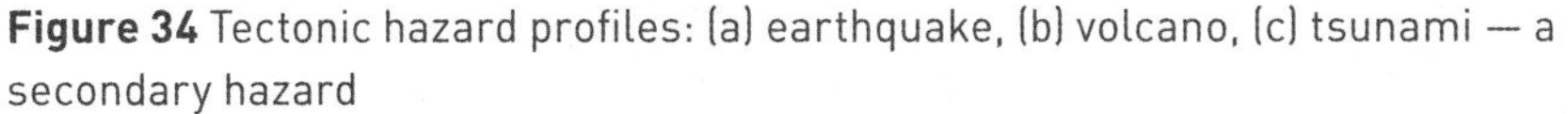

Figure 34 Tectonic hazard profiles: (a) earthquake, (b) volcano, (c) tsunami — a secondary hazard

Table 9 Abridged modified Mercalli intensity scale

Average peak velocity ($cm\,s^{-1}$)	Intensity value and description
	I Not felt, except by a very few under exceptionally favourable circumstances
1–2	**II** Felt only by a few persons at rest, especially on upper floors of buildings. Delicately suspended objects may swing
2–5	**III** Felt quite noticeably indoors, especially on upper floors of buildings, but many people do not recognise it as an earthquake. Standing automobiles may rock slightly. Vibration like passing truck. Duration estimated
5–8	**IV** During day felt indoors by many, outdoors by few. At night some awakened. Dishes, windows, doors disturbed; walls make creaking sound. Sensation like heavy truck striking building. Standing automobiles rocked noticeably
8–12	**V** Felt by nearly everyone, many awakened. Some dishes, windows etc. broken; cracked plaster in a few places; unstable objects overturned. Disturbance of trees, poles and other tall objects sometimes noticed. Pendulum clocks may stop
	VI Felt by all, many frightened and run outdoors. Some heavy furniture moved; a few instances of fallen plaster and damaged chimneys. Damage slight
20–30	**VII** Everybody runs outdoors. Damage negligible in buildings of good design and construction; slight to moderate in well-built ordinary structure; considerable in poorly built or badly designed structures; some chimneys broken. Noticed by persons driving cars
45–55	**VIII** Damage slight in specially designed structures; considerable in ordinary substantial buildings, with partial collapse; great in poorly built structures. Panel walls thrown out of frame structure. Fall of chimneys, factory stacks, columns, walls, monuments. Heavy furniture overturned. Sand and mud ejected in small amounts. Changes in well water. Persons driving cars disturbed
> 60	**IX** Damage considerable in specially designed structures; well-designed frame structures thrown out of plumb; damage great in substantial buildings, with partial collapse. Buildings shifted off foundations. Ground cracked conspicuously. Underground pipes broken
	X Some well-built wooden structures destroyed; most masonry and frame structures destroyed including foundations; ground badly cracked. Rails bent. Landslides considerable from river banks and steep slopes. Shifted sand and mud. Water splashed, slopped over banks
	XI Few, if any (masonry) structures remain standing. Bridges destroyed. Broad fissures in ground. Underground pipelines completely out of surface. Earth slumps and landslips in soft ground. Rails bend greatly
	XII Damage total. Waves seen on ground surface. Lines of sight and level distorted. Objects thrown into the air

Table 10 The relationship between earthquake magnitude and number of deaths resulting

Date	Region	Magnitude	Deaths
2011, March 11	East coast of Honshu, Japan	9.0	28,050
2010, January 12	Port-au-Prince, Haiti	7.0	220,000
2009, September 30	Southern Sumatra, Indonesia	7.5	1,117
2008, May 12	Eastern Sichuan, China	7.9	87,587
2006, May 26	Java, Indonesia	6.3	5,749
2005, October 8	Kashmir, E Pakistan/northwest India	7.6	73,000
2004, December 26	Sumatra and Indian Ocean	9.1	227,898
2003, December 26	Bam, southeast Iran	6.6	30,000
2002, March 25	Hindu Kush, Afghanistan	6.1	1,000
2001, January 21	Gujarat, northwest India	7.9	20,023

Magnitude of volcanic eruptions

All volcanoes are formed from molten material (magma) in the Earth's crust. There is no fully agreed scale for measuring the size of eruptions, but Newhall and Self (1982) drew up a semi-quantitative **volcanic explosivity index** (**VEI**), which can be related to the type of magma that influences the type of eruption. It combined:

- the total volume of ejected products
- the height of the eruption cloud
- the duration of the main eruptive phase
- several other items such as eruption rate

into a basic 0–8 scale of increasing hazard. The results can be related to the type of volcanic eruption.

For example, the 1991 eruption of Mt Pinatubo in the Philippines was a **Plinian type** of eruption with a plume of tephra ejected more than 30 km into the atmosphere and was classified as a VEI 5–6. The VEI is, despite all the measurements, only a partly quantitative scale and it has several important limitations. For example, all types of ejected material are treated alike, and no account is taken of SO_2 emissions, which are needed to quantify the impact of eruptions on climate change. Most of the very large eruptions (VEI 6–8) happened in geological time. Measuring the scale of volcanic eruptions is challenging as there are so many different types. Table 11 shows how volcanic eruptions can be classified using the VEI.

Table 11 The volcanic explosion index (VEI) scale

Volcanic explosivity index (VEI)	Eruption rate (kg s^{-1})	Volume of ejecta (m^3)	Eruption column height (km)	Duration of continuous blasts (h)	Troposphere/ stratosphere injection	Qualitative description	Example
0 Non-explosive	10^2–10^3	<10^4	0.8–1.5	<1	Negligible/ none	Effusive	Kilauea, erupts continuously
1 Small	10^3–10^4	10^4–10^6	1.5–2.8	<1	Minor/none	Gentle	Nyiragongo, 2002
2 Moderate	10^4–10^5	10^6–10^7	2.8–5.5	1–6	Moderate/ none	Explosive	Galeras, Columbia, 1993
3 Moderate-large	10^5–10^6	10^7–10^8	5.5–10.5	1–12	Great/possible	Severe	Nevada del Ruiz, 1985
4 Large	10^6–10^7	10^8–10^9	10.5–17.0	1–>12	Great/definite	Violent	Mayon, 1895 Eyjafjallajökull, 2010
5 Very large	10^7–10^8	10^9–10^{10}	17.0–28.0	6–>12	Great/ significant	Cataclysmic	Vesuvius, AD79 Mt St Helens, 1980
6 Very large	10^8–10^9	10^{10}–10^{11}	28.0–47.0	>12	Great/ significant	Paroxysmal	Mt Pinatubo, 1991
7 Very large	>10^9	10^{11}–10^{12}	>47.0	>12	Great/ significant	Colossal	Tambora, 1815
8 Very large	–	>10^{12}	–	>12	Great/ significant	Terrific	Yellowstone, millions of years ago

Note that the VEI is a logarithmic scale, because each step of the scale represents a ten-fold increase in material ejected.

Magnitude is largely measureable (easier for earthquakes) and can clearly influence impact.

Frequency

Frequency (i.e. how often an event occurs) is sometimes called the **recurrence** level, e.g. for a 1 in 100 year event. There is an inverse relationship between frequency and magnitude, i.e. the larger the magnitude of the event, the less frequent its occurrence. The effect of frequency on severity of impact is difficult to gauge. Theoretically, areas that experience frequent tectonic events have both adaptation and mitigation measures in place, including extensive monitoring (useful for volcanoes), education and community awareness about what to do (useful for earthquakes or tsunami evacuation routes), and various technological strategies for shockproof building design (Tokyo, San Francisco) or protection (Japanese tsunami walls). It is well known that unexpected tectonic events, such as the 1993 Killari earthquake, can be particularly devastating. On the other hand, familiarity with a frequently erupting volcano, such as Mt Merapi in Indonesia, can breed contempt, as local people are so used to its eruptions that they do not always evacuate soon enough.

Areal extent

Areal extent is the size of the area covered by the tectonic hazard and this has a clear impact (see Figure 35).

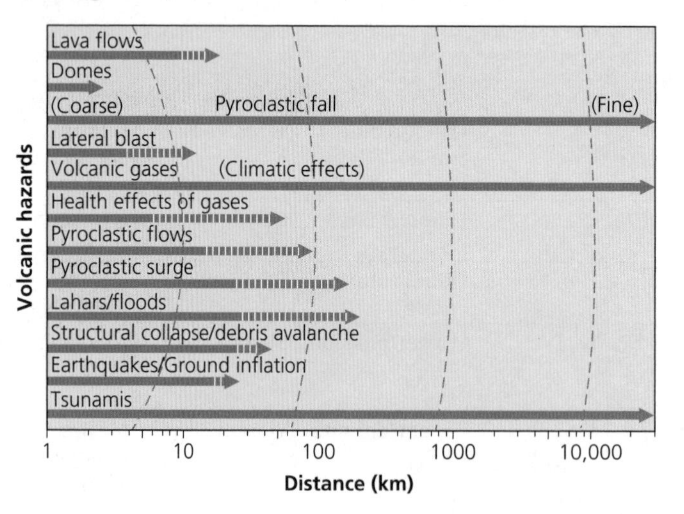

Figure 35 The areal extent of the impacts of various features of a volcanic eruption

Spatial concentration

Spatial concentration is the areal distribution of tectonic hazards over geographical space. It is controlled largely by type of plate boundary. In theory, permanent settlement is avoided in hazardous regions but often such locations present other opportunities, for example some volcanic soils are very fertile, so agricultural settlement occurs, such as on the flanks of Mt Merapi, Indonesia. Equally spring water may be available, such as at Bam, the site of a severe earthquake. Active tectonic, especially volcanic, landscapes encourage tourism, as was seen in the recent unexpected Japanese eruption (Ontaki), where many of the 48 dead were hikers.

Duration

Duration is the length of time for which the tectonic hazard exists. Often an initial earthquake event is followed by massive aftershocks (e.g. Christchurch 2010 and central Italy, 2014) or a series of eruptions occurs. While individual earthquakes often last for only around 30 seconds, the damage can be extensive.

Knowledge check 33

Define the term 'aftershock' and explain its significance for the Christchurch earthquakes.

Secondary hazards often prolong the duration of impact and increase the damage, for example the Tohoku multi-disaster (earthquake, tsunami and nuclear accident). Secondary hazards associated with volcanic eruptions include **lahars** (e.g. Mt Pinatubo; see p. 76) or **jökulhlaup** (glacier bursts) (see p. 77), which are very damaging because of their spatial and temporal unpredictability. In November 1985, the melting of the ice cap and snow on Nevada del Ruiz volcano (p. 79) released huge mudflows that overwhelmed Armero and the surrounding villages, killing 23,000 people. Locally, Himalayan earthquakes such as Kashmir 2005 and Sichuan 2008, cause widespread landslides that disrupt rescue and recovery and add to the death toll.

Speed of onset

Speed of onset can be a crucial factor. Earthquakes generally come with little warning. The speed of onset and the almost immediate shaking of the ground led to maximum destruction by the Kobe earthquake, but this was allied with other factors such as timing and building type. The 2004 Boxing Day tsunami illustrates the variation well (see p. 104) with little awareness of the hazard possible at Aceh, Indonesia, but, theoretically, warnings and therefore evacuation were possible everywhere else. This was in spite of a lack of a sophisticated warning system (subsequently built) for the Indian Ocean, unlike that which existed in the Pacific Ocean, based on Hawaii.

Predictability of occurrence

The random temporal distribution of both earthquakes and volcanoes can add to their potential impact. While **gap theory** can increase the possibility of predicting the 'Big One', in reality earthquakes are unpredictable. Volcanic eruptions can also be hard to predict precisely, even with close monitoring, hence discussions concerning the possible and long-awaited eruption of Vesuvius in the densely settled Bay of Naples.

Knowledge check 34

Explain seismic gap theory and its role in earthquake prediction.

Summary

- The Earth's structure has a number of layers: the inner core, outer core, mantle and crust, each with different densities, chemical composition and physical properties.
- The theory of plate tectonics states that the Earth's surface is made up of rigid plates, 'floating' on the asthenosphere. It was thought that their movement was powered by convection currents from radioactive decay in the Earth's core, but today it is thought that gravitational sliding is the force driving plate movement and slab pull is the key mechanism.
- Plates move in three ways: diverging at a constructive margin, converging at a destructive margin, or making a transform movement at a conservative margin. These movements occur under the oceans and on the continents with different results.

- Hotspots are small areas of the crust with an unusually high heat flow, away from plate boundaries.
- The main zones of earthquakes closely follow the plate boundaries but intra-plate earthquakes and quasi-natural earthquakes generated by human activity, also occur.
- Active volcanoes are found along constructive plate boundaries, destructive plate boundaries and at hotspots.
- The characteristics of the physical hazard profile that influence its impact include magnitude (Mercalli and Richter scales and volcanic explosivity index), predictability, frequency, duration, speed of onset and areal extent.

Volcanoes, processes, hazards and their impacts

Types of volcanoes

Volcanoes can be classified by their **shape** and the nature of the **vent** the magma is extruded through, as well as the nature of the **eruption**.

Shape of the volcano and its vent

Figure 36 shows how volcanoes can be classified by shape. The shape is, of course, largely dependent on the material erupted, which itself can be linked back to the tectonic setting.

- **Fissure eruptions** result when lava is ejected through tensional linear fissures, rather than a central vent, at divergent plate boundaries. The Haimeay eruption in Iceland of 1973 began with a fissure 2 km long, through which lava poured effusively.

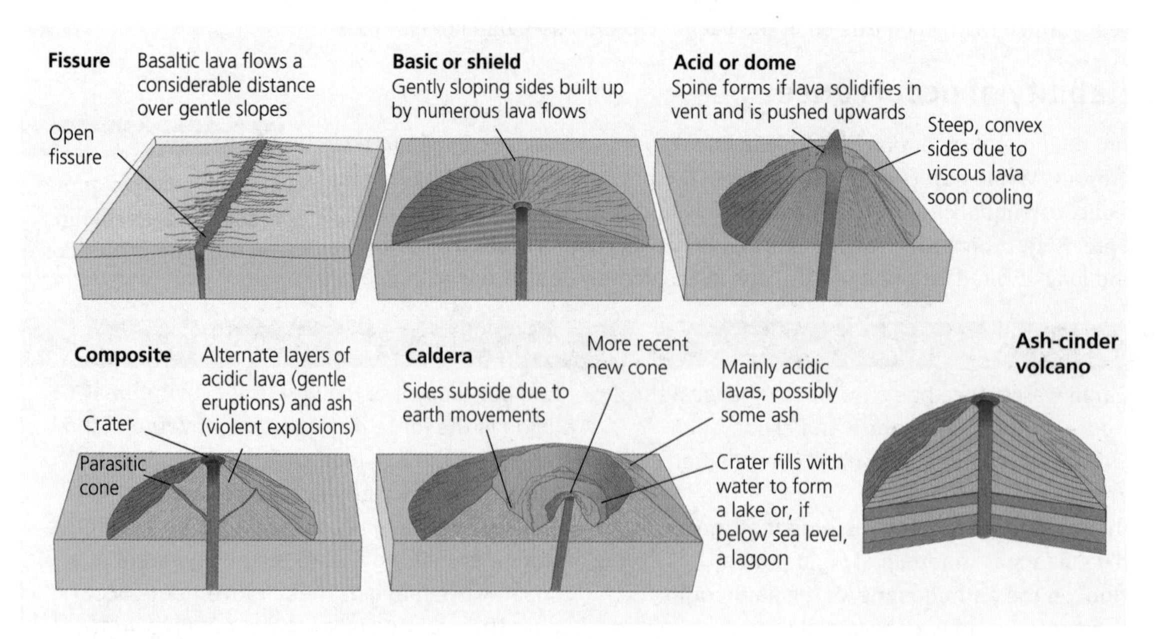

Figure 36 Types of volcano by shape

- **Shield volcanoes**, such as Mauna Kea in Hawaii, are formed when basaltic lava pours in huge quantities out of a central vent. Because of the effusive nature of the basic fluid lava, it can spread over a wide area before solidifying. The result is a huge volcanic cone but with gently sloping sides. The lava has low viscosity because of its low (<50%) silica content, and erupts at temperatures of about 1200°C. Mauna Loa in Hawaii has built up a cone that rises 9000 m from the sea floor, with a diameter of 120 km at its base, sloping at about 6° to the top. Shield volcanoes occur at both oceanic diverging plates and hotspots.
- **Composite cones or strato-volcanoes** form from alternating layers of lava and ash, resulting from eruptions at destructive plate margins. The lava itself is typically acidic with more than 50% silica content. It has a temperature of about 800°C. This means it flows more slowly, creating cones with more steeply sloping sides. The ash is produced in a highly explosive eruptive phase, often after the vent has been blocked. Many of the world's well known volcanoes, such as Mt Etna, Vesuvius and Popocatepetl, are composite volcanoes. Etna is a classic cone shape with slopes of 50° near its base, but slopes of only 30° at the summit, with a marked crater.
- **Acid or dome volcanoes** result when acid lava quickly solidifies on exposure to the air. These volcanoes frequently have parasitic cones formed as the passage of the rising rhyolitic magma through the main vent is blocked. The cones are steep sided and convex in shape. In one extreme example (Mt Pelée) the lava actually solidified as it came up the vent, producing a spine, rather than flowing down the sides.
- **Ash and cinder cones** such as Paricutin are formed when ash and cinders build up in a cylindrical cone of relatively small size. They are highly permeable as they are composed of loose volcanic cinders. A typical size is 800 m in height, with a bowl-shaped crater.
- **Calderas** occur when the build-up of gases becomes extreme. Huge explosions may clear the magma chamber beneath the volcano and remove the summit of the cone, or cauldron subsidence may occur. This causes the sides of the crater to collapse and subside, thus widening the opening to several kilometres in diameter. Frequently, enlarged craters or calderas have been flooded and later eruptions have formed smaller cones in the resulting lake, e.g. Wizard Island in Crater Lake Oregon.

Nature of the eruption

The nature of the eruption is also significant. Table 12 summarises the major categories of eruption, based on the degree of violence/explosivity, a consequence of pressure and the amount of gas in the magma.

Table 12 Major categories of eruption

	Category	Description
Effusive	Icelandic	Lava flows directly from a fissure
	Hawaiian	Lava is emitted gently from a vent
	Strombolian	Small but frequent eruptions occur
	Vulcanian	More violent and less frequent
	Vesuvian	Violent explosion after a long period of inactivity
	Krakatoan	Exceptionally violent explosion
	Pelean	Violent eruption of pyroclastic flows (nuées ardentes)
Explosive	Plinian	Large amounts of lava and pyroclastic material are ejected

Exam tip

Match the eruption types to the VEI scale. Always have a named example ready for each eruption type.

Volcanic processes and the production of associated hazards

Pyroclastic flows and surges

Pyroclastic flows have been responsible for most volcanic deaths to date. They are sometimes called **nuées ardentes** ('glowing clouds') and result from frothing of the molten magma in the volcano vent. Bubbles in the magma burst explosively to eject a lethal mixture of hot gases and pyroclastic material (volcanic fragments, ash, pumice and glass shapes). Pyroclastic bursts surge downhill because, as they contain a heavy load of rock fragment and dust, they are denser than the surrounding air. The clouds may be literally red hot (up to 1000°C). The greatest risks occur when the summit crater is blocked by viscous rhyolitic magma and blasts are directed laterally in Peléan type eruptions, in surges of $30\,m\,s^{-1}$, close to the ground and up to 30–40 km from the source.

There is little warning of these events; people exposed are killed immediately by severe external and internal burns combined with asphyxiation. The cloud which hit the town of St Pierre, Martinique (6 km from the centre of the VEI 6 eruption) in the Mont Pelée disaster of 1902 had a temperature of 700°C and travelled at $33\,m\,s^{-1}$ down the River Blanche Valley. All but three of the inhabitants of St Pierre (around 30,000 in all) were killed. One was saved by being in the jail!

Lava flows

While lava flows are spectacular, they pose more threat to property than human life (e.g. eruptions of Kilauea, the destruction of much of the village of Kapilani, covering $78\,km^2$ and destroying nearly 200 houses). The lava flows most dangerous to human life come from fissure eruptions, not central vents, as highly fluid basalt magma can move down a hillside at $50\,km\,h^{-1}$ and can spread a long way from the source. One deadly lava flow erupted from Nyiragongo volcano's flanks, draining the lava lake which had collected at the summit; it killed 72 people and devastated the town of Goma in the Democratic Republic of the Congo.

Pahoehoe lava is the most liquid of all lava, and tends to form a ropey wrinkled surface. On steep slopes this low viscosity lava can move downhill at speeds approaching $15\,m\,s^{-1}$.

A'a lava tends to form blocks, and moves more slowly downhill, leaving a rough irregular surface.

The greatest lava-related disaster in historic times occurred in 1783 when huge quantities of lava poured out of the 24 km long Laki fissure in Iceland. Although there were few direct deaths the resultant famines from lack of crop growth killed more than 10,000 people, around 20% of Iceland's population.

Airfall tephra (ash falls)

Tephra consists of all the fragmented material ejected by the volcano which subsequently falls to the ground. The large explosive eruptions of Mt St Helens (VEI 5) produced an estimated 6 km^3 volume of material, which covered a wide area of northwest USA. The particles ranged in size from so-called 'bombs' (>32 m in diameter) down to fine ash and dust (<4 mm in diameter). Coarser, heavier particles fall out of the sky close to the volcano vent. Occasionally tephra is sufficiently hot to spontaneously combust and start fires. Ash clouds can be blown many miles away from the original eruption by strong winds.

Large eruptions such as Krakatoa (VEI 6) in 1883, which spread an aerosol cloud around the globe within 2 weeks, and Tambora, Indonesia 1816 (VEI 7), which led to short-term global cooling of around 1–2 years, could be prolonged to a decadal scale by successive eruptions.

Although ash falls account for fewer than 5% of direct deaths associated with volcanic eruptions (usually respiratory problems), they can create a number of problems.

- Heavy falls of cinders and ash can blanket the landscape, contaminating farmland and poisoning livestock.
- Ash causes health issues such as skin abrasion and breathing problems (silicosis, chronic obstructive pulmonary disease (COPD)).
- The weight of ash can damage roofs.
- Ash washes into lakes and rivers to become a lahar source.
- Wet ash conducts electricity and can cause failure of electronic equipment.
- Fine ash can clog air filters and damage vehicles and aero engines.
- Ash can lead to vehicle accidents, poor visibility, slippery roads.

Exam tip

Research the 2010 Eyjafjallajökull eruption, which had a huge impact on the world economy because it brought flights to a standstill, with enormous global impacts. It is a unique case study.

Volcanic gases

Large amounts and a wide range of gases are released from explosive eruptions and from cooling lava. The complex gas mixture includes water vapour, hydrogen, carbon monoxide, carbon dioxide, hydrogen sulphate, sulphur dioxide, chlorine and hydrogen chloride in variable amounts.

Carbon monoxide causes deaths because of its toxic effects at very low concentrations, but most fatalities have been associated with carbon dioxide (CO_2) releases, because CO_2 is colourless and odourless. In Indonesia, as villagers were evacuating following the eruption of Mt Merapi, they walked into a dense pool of volcanically released CO_2 which had sunk (it is denser than air); 140 were asphyxiated.

The release of CO_2 from past volcanic activity can also create a highly unusual threat. In 1984 a cloud of gas, rich in CO_2, burst out of the volcanic crater of Lake Monoun, Cameroon, killing 37 people. Two years later in 1986, a similar disaster occurred at Lake Nyos crater, Cameroon, killing 1746 people and more than 8000 livestock. The outburst of gas created a fountain that reached 100 m above the lake, before the dense cloud flowed down two valleys to cover an area of more than 60 km^2.

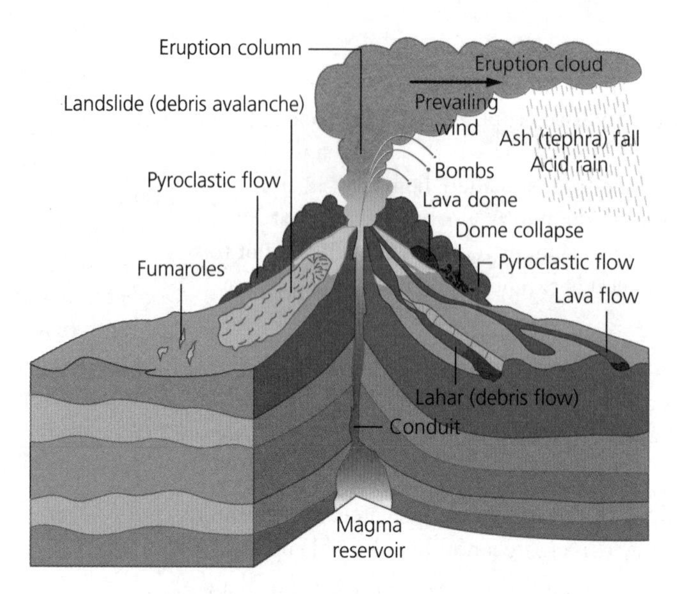

Figure 37 Types of volcanic hazard

These rare hazards are the result of unusually high levels of CO_2 in the volcanic lakes. The levels probably build up over a long period of time from CO_2-rich groundwater springs flowing into the submerged craters.

Secondary volcanic hazards

Lahars

After pyroclastic flows, lahars present the greatest risk to human life. They can be defined as volcanic mudflows composed of largely silt-size sediments. Lahars consist of volcanic ash and rock up to at least 40% by weight, combined with the torrential rain which often accompanies volcanic eruptions. They create dense, viscous flows that can travel even faster than clear-water streams. They occur widely on steep volcanic flanks, especially in tropical humid or monsoon climates (*lahar* is an Indonesian term).

The degree of hazard varies greatly but generally the flows that contain the larger size sediments are the more deadly. At Mt Pinatubo in the Philippines, lahars regularly transport and deposit tens of millions of cubic metres of sediment in a day and are a potential threat to the local population of over 100,000 people.

Lahars can be classified as **primary**, occurring directly during a volcanic eruption (usually **hot flows**), and **secondary**, which are triggered by high intensity rainfall between eruptions which reactivate old flows of ash etc.

Some lahars are generated by rapid melting of snow and ice — a particular hazard in northern Andean volcanoes. The second deadliest disaster in recent times was caused by the eruption of Nevada del Ruiz volcano (see p. 79).

Knowledge check 35

Using examples, distinguish between primary, secondary and tertiary tectonic hazards.

Volcanic landslides

Landslides and debris avalanches are a common feature of volcano-related ground failure. They are particularly associated with eruptions of siliceous acidic dacitic magma of relatively high viscosity with a large content of dissolved gas.

Volcanic landslides are gravity-driven slides of masses of rock and loose volcanic material. They can occur during an eruption, such as Mt St Helens when the side of the volcano collapsed to form massive landslides and debris avalanches containing 2.7 km^3 of material. They can be set off as a result of heavy rainfall or, more commonly, earthquakes.

Ground deformation of volcanic slopes by rising magma, which creates a bulge, can also trigger slope instability and landslides before an eruption, e.g. prior to the Mt St Helens events. Swarms of small earthquakes there were followed by ground uplift and the formation of a huge bulge prior to the main eruption, and then the final trigger of a more major post-bulge earthquake.

Jökulhlaups

In most subglacial eruptions, the water produced from melting ice becomes trapped in a lake between the volcano and the overlying glacier. Eventually this water is released as a violent and potentially dangerous flood. As events of this type are so common in Iceland the Icelanders have coined the term jökulhlaup, which means glacial outburst. One of the most dramatic jökulhlaups to ever occur was a result of an eruption of Grimsvotn in 1996. Over a month, more than 3 m^3 of meltwater accumulated beneath the Vatnajökull ice cap. The subglacial lake suddenly burst out, some of the water escaping beneath the ice cap and some spouting out through a side fissure. The resulting flood was temporarily the second biggest flow of water in the world (after the River Amazon). It caused US$14 million of damage and left numerous icebergs scattered across Iceland's southern coastal plain. However, jökulhlaups rarely turn into disasters as they occur in remote unpopulated areas.

Note: **tsunamis** (see pp. 82–83) can occur after catastrophic volcanic eruptions as well as earthquakes, but more rarely so — only 5% of tsunamis are generated by volcanic activity. For example, the structural failure of the volcanic island Krakatoa (VEI 6) in 1883 created a debris flow big enough to produce a tsunami.

Impacts of volcanic hazards on people and the built environment

The impact of volcanic hazards depends on a number of factors, including the **physical profile** of the volcanic event (see p. 67), the status of the volcano — whether it is extinct, dormant or active — as well as key factors such as population density, level of development, standard of governance, timing of eruption, and presence or absence of mitigation strategies.

Exam tip

Impacts should be illustrated by 'mini' case studies. These short fact files provide useful supporting evidence in an exam to add locational knowledge to your answer.

Knowledge check 36

Define 'active', 'dormant' and 'extinct' volcanoes.

Environmental impacts at local, regional and global scales (for A-level study)

The **environmental** impacts of explosive volcanic eruptions are largely related to weather and climate, as shown in Table 13.

Table 13 The effects of large explosive volcanic eruptions on weather and climate

Effect	Mechanism	Begins	Duration	Scale
Increased precipitation	H_2O given off in large quantities during eruption	During eruption	1–4 days, i.e. period of eruption	Local
Reduction of diurnal cycle	Blockage of short-wave and emission of long-wave radiation	Immediately	1–4 days	Local
Reduced tropical precipitation	Blockage of short-wave radiation, reduced evaporation	1–3 months	3–6 months	Regional
Summer cooling of northern hemisphere, tropics and sub-tropics	Blockage of short-wave radiation	1–3 months	1–2 years	Regional
Stratospheric warming	Stratospheric absorption of short-wave and long-wave radiation	1–3 months	1–2 years	Global
Winter warming of northern hemisphere continents	Stratospheric absorption of short-wave and long-wave radiation	6 months	1 or 2 winters	Regional
Global cooling	Blockage of short-wave radiation	Immediately	1–3 years	Global
Global cooling from multiple eruptions	Blockage of short-wave radiation	Immediately	10 years	Global
Ozone depletion, enhanced ultraviolet	Dilution, heterogeneous chemistry and aerosols	1 day	1–2 years	Global

Demographic, economic and social impacts of volcanic hazards on people and the built environment

In general, over a 25 year period, volcanoes are comparatively minor hazards compared with other geo hazards and all natural disasters (Table 14).

Table 14 Average losses per year in natural disasters 1975–2000

	Volcanoes	Earthquakes	All natural disasters
People dead	1,019	18,416	84,034
People injured	285	27,585	65,296
People made homeless	15,128	239,265	4,856,586
People affected	94,399	1,590,314	144 million
Estimated damage (US$ billions)	0.065	21.5	62.0

Volcanic hazards are volcanic events with the potential to cause harm, loss or detriment to humans, and the things humans value.

hazard event × vulnerability of people = adverse consequences, harm or loss

Figure 38 shows a damage map and table for the Nevado del Ruiz eruption, which devastated the local area and the overall economy of Colombia.

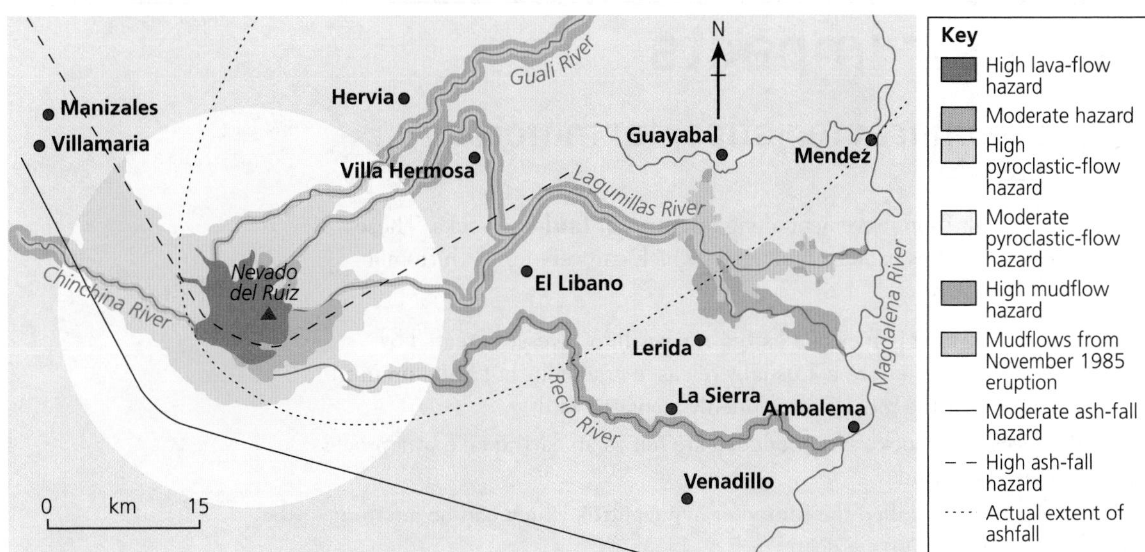

Category of loss	Details
Deaths and injuries	Nearly 70% of the population of Armero killed (20,000 approx.) and a further 17% (5000) injured
Agricultural	60% of the region's livestock, 30% of sorghum and rice crops, and 500,000 bags of coffee destroyed. Over 3400 ha of agricultural land lost from production
Communications	Virtually all roads, bridges, telephone lines and power supplies in the area destroyed. Whole region isolated
Industrial, commercial and civic buildings	50 schools, two hospitals, 58 industrial plants, 343 commercial establishments and the National Coffee Research Centre badly damaged or destroyed
Housing	Most homes destroyed. 8000 people made homeless
Monetary	Cost to the economy estimated at US$7.7 billion, or 20% of the country's GNP for that year

Figure 38 Damage map and table for Nevado del Ruiz, Colombia

Knowledge check 37

Summarise the factors that explain why Nevado del Ruiz was one of the most devastating volcanic hazards.

Exam tip

Always apply your case studies to the specific question — avoid narrative description.

Summary

- Volcanoes can be classified by shape, type of vent and type of eruption. They include shield, composite, cinder cones, fissure eruptions, acid or dome volcanoes and calderas. Eruptions range from explosive to effusive.
- Volcanic processes and associated hazards include pyroclastic flows, lava flows, ash falls, lahars, jökulhlaups, landslides and toxic gases.
- The demographic, economic and social impacts of volcanic hazards depend on physical factors such as the nature of the volcanic event, the status of the volcano, and human factors such as population density, level of development, governance and mitigation strategies.
- Environmental impacts of explosive volcanic eruptions mainly affect weather and climate.
- Volcanic hazards affect people and property and have impacts at global, regional and local scales.
- You will need to learn one (AS) or two (A-level) examples of eruptions to demonstrate the varied degree of risk and impacts of volcanic activity.

Earthquakes, processes, hazards and their impacts

Earthquake characteristics, terminology and causes

Most earthquakes result from movement along fractures or **faults** in rocks. These faults usually occur in groups called a fault zone, which can vary in width from a metre to several kilometres.

Movement occurs along fault planes of all sizes as a result of stresses created by crustal movement. The stresses are not usually released gradually, but build up until they become so great that the rocks shift suddenly along the fault.

- As the fault moves, the shockwaves produced are felt as an earthquake by a process known as **elastic rebound**.
- The point of the break is called the **focus** (or hypocentre), which can be anything from a few kilometres to 700 km deep.
- If the stresses are released in small stages there may be a series of small earthquakes.
- Conversely, if the stresses build up without being released, there is the possibility of a 'Big One' — a major earthquake.

Often, as in the case of Christchurch, many of these faults are buried, so it is difficult to predict earthquakes when there is no knowledge of their existence.

During an earthquake, the extent of ground shaking is measured by motion seismometers activated by strong ground tremors, which record both horizontal and vertical ground accelerations caused by the shaking.

Analysis of data collected from the seismographs shows that earthquakes produce four main types of seismic waves, which are summarised in Table 15.

Table 15 Types of seismic waves

Primary (P) waves	P waves are vibrations caused by compression. They spread out from the earthquake fault at a rate of about 8 km s^{-1} and travel through both solid rock (Earth's core) and liquids (oceans)
Secondary (S) waves	S waves move through the Earth's body at about half the speed of P waves. They vibrate at right angles to the direction of travel. S waves, which cannot travel through liquids, are responsible for a lot of earthquake damage
Rayleigh (R) waves	R waves are surface waves in which particles follow an elliptical path in the direction of propagation and partly in a vertical plane — like water moving with an ocean wave
Love (L) waves	L waves are similar to R waves but move faster and have vibration solely in the horizontal plain. They often generate the greatest damage, as unreinforced masonry buildings cannot cope with horizontal accelerations

The overall severity of an earthquake is dependent on the amplitude and frequency of these wave motions. S and L waves are more destructive than P waves because they have a larger amplitude and force. Therefore, in an earthquake the ground surface may be displaced horizontally, vertically or obliquely, depending on wave activity and geological conditions.

The recorded time intervals between the arrival of the waves at different seismogram stations are used to locate the **epicentre** (the point in the Earth's surface directly above the **focus** of an earthquake).

Three broad categories of earthquake focus, by **depth**, are recognised:

1 deep focus 300–700 km
2 intermediate focus 70–300 km
3 shallow focus 0–70 km. These are the most common (around 75%) and cause the most damage.

Knowledge check 38

Distinguish between the epicentre and focus of an earthquake.

Earthquake processes and hazards

Primary hazards

Ground movement and ground shaking

Surface seismic waves represent the most severe hazard to humans and their activities, since buildings and other structures may collapse and kill or injure their occupants. Ground motion severs underground pipes and power lines, resulting in fires and explosions, especially from escaping gas (1907 San Francisco earthquake). Ruptured water pipes mean that often it is difficult to extinguish these fires.

Near the epicentre, ground motion is both severe and complex, as there is an interlocking pattern of both P and S waves and, theoretically, most damage should occur at the epicentre. Different surface materials respond in different ways to the surface waves, with unconsolidated sediments being most affected because they amplify the shaking. This leads to differential damage of buildings and infrastructure, based not only on distance from the epicentre but also on surface materials (local geological conditions). Steep topography, as in San Francisco, also amplifies 'waves'.

This differential damage was apparent in the Mercalli earthquake intensity levels for the Lomo Prieta earthquake (MM 7.1 in 1988). More than 98% of economic losses were a result of ground shaking, and 41 out of 67 deaths resulted when ground shaking caused the upper tier of the Nimitz freeway in Oakland to collapse because it was constructed on foundations of soft mud and bay fill material.

The phrase 'buildings kill, not earthquakes' is meaningful when considering earthquakes with severe impacts. Building quality is key. Poorly built, unreinforced structures with heavy, tiled roofs are the most dangerous. In the 1988 Armenian earthquake (MM 6.9) 25,000 people were killed, 31,000 were injured and 500,000 were made homeless within a 50 km radius of the epicentre. Distance decay was clearly shown in that 88% of the older stone buildings were destroyed in Spitak, only 5 km from the epicentre, but only 38% in Leninakan, 35 km from the epicentre.

However, in Leninakan, 95% of the more modern 9–12 storey Soviet-built pre-cast concrete frame buildings were destroyed (they had soft foundations and no earthquake proofing). In the 2008 Sichuan earthquake (MM 7.9), although the ground shaking formed a linear pattern extending along the Longmen Shan Fault, a large number of pre-cast concrete school buildings were completely destroyed, scattered over a wide area, with other buildings remaining comparatively unaffected. This hit the headlines because, as a result of China's one-child policy, many families lost their only child.

The **duration** of shaking is also important — longer periods of shaking causing more damage for the same magnitude event.

Knowledge check 39

Explain how China's one-child policy exacerbated the tragedy of the Sichuan earthquake.

Secondary hazards

Liquefaction

Liquefaction is an important secondary hazard that is associated with loose sediments. This is the process by which water-saturated material can lose strength and behave as a fluid when subjected to strong ground shaking which increases pore water pressures. Poorly compacted sands and silts situated at depths less than 10 m below the surface are most affected when saturated with water.

In the earthquakes at Christchurch, New Zealand (2010), Mexico City (1985) and Valdez, Alaska (1964) liquefaction that caused buildings and infrastructure to collapse was a notable hazard, resulting in an almost random pattern of building destruction.

Landslides, rock and snow avalanches

Severe ground shaking causes natural slopes to weaken and fail. The resulting landslides, rock and snow avalanches can make a major contribution to earthquake disasters, especially in mountain areas such as the Himalayas. These landslides hamper relief efforts, as in the Kashmir earthquake or the Nepal Gorkha earthquake in 2015. It is estimated that landslides can double earthquake deaths, especially with high magnitude earthquakes because they can occur over a huge area.

Landslide risk post-earthquake varies with differences in topography, rainfall, soil and land use (whether forested or not). An example of an earthquake-generated rock slide occurred in Peru in 1970 as a massive rock avalanche broke away from the overhanging face of the Huascaran Mountain. A turbulent flow of mud and boulders flowed down the Santa valley, forming a wave 50 m high, travelling at an average speed of 70–100 m s^{-1}. The towns of Yungay and Ranatirca were buried under debris 10 m deep, killing 18,000 people in four minutes. Flooding can occur, as it did in Sichuan when numerous landslides dammed temporary lakes which subsequently burst through, causing flash flooding. The recent aftershocks of earthquakes in central Italy generated avalanches after heavy snow.

Tsunamis

Tsunamis are the most destructive secondary earthquake-related hazard. Most tsunamis are generated at subduction–convergent plate boundaries, with 90% of damaging tsunamis occurring in the Pacific Basin (hence the establishment of the Pacific Warning System). Exceptions include the 2004 Boxing Day tsunami in the Indian Ocean. The most active tsunami source area is the Japan–Taiwan islands (over 25% of tsunamis).

Tsunamis occur if an earthquake rupture occurs under the ocean or in a coastal zone, if the focus is not deep within the Earth's crust, and if the magnitude of the earthquake (6+) is large enough to create significant vertical displacement. A tsunami is a series of ocean waves that 'spread out' from the earthquake focus, carrying large volumes of water, and debris too once they reach land.

Knowledge check 40

Explain why only certain earthquakes cause tsunamis.

The intensity (magnitude) of tsunamis can be measured by a descriptive, observational scale devised by Soloviev in 1978, which is based on the run-up height.

In the last 100 years, more than 2000 tsunamis have killed over 500,000 people (over 50% in the mega disaster of the 2004 Boxing Day tsunami, which was the most deadly tsunami recorded).

A number of physical factors influence the degree of devastation, including wave energy, which is dependent on water depth, the process of shoaling, the shape of the coastline, the topography of the land and the presence or absence of natural defences such as coral reefs or mangroves. Human factors include the population profile, the degree of coastal development, the cohesiveness of the society and people's experience of the tsunami hazard, as well as the presence or absence of warning systems and evacuation plans.

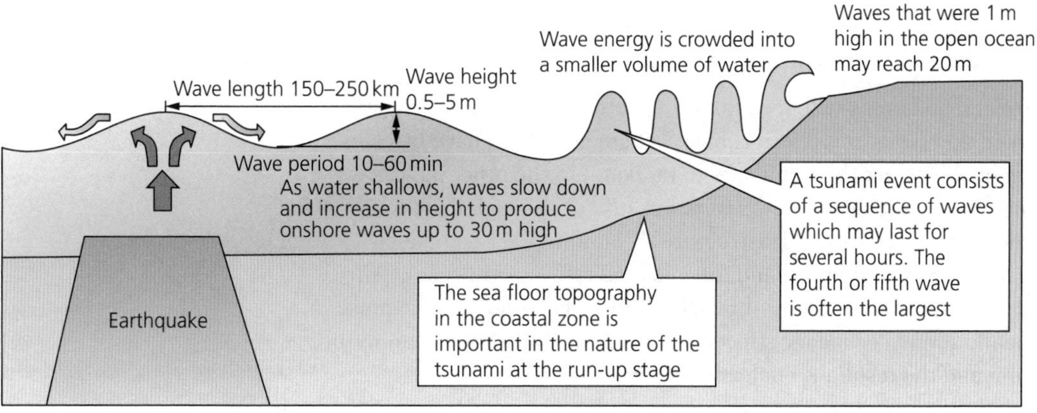

Figure 39 The formation and key features of a tsunami

Demographic, economic and social impacts of earthquakes on people and the built environment

There are a number of differences between the impacts of volcanoes and earthquakes with their related tsunamis. In comparison with volcanoes, earthquakes can be much more deadly and their impacts more selective in terms of damage to buildings and deaths of people.

The **primary** effects of a major earthquake are the immediate consequences, such as damage to houses from shaking or fires, and instantaneous deaths of people hit by falling tiles and roofs. On the streets, cracks form across roads and bridges collapse; there is widespread destruction of gas mains and water pipes; and severe fractures of or the concertina downwards of badly built concrete high-rise blocks. Within a few minutes people are trapped and injured; many die quickly.

The **secondary** effects of an earthquake are those that manifest in the days, weeks and even months after an earthquake event. Air pollution might result from burning fires and combustion from leaking gas mains. Contamination from sewage is another serious secondary danger, causing diseases such as typhoid or cholera as a result of a shortage of clean water. After the 2010 Haiti earthquake 738,979 cases of cholera were reported, leading to 421,410 hospitalisations and nearly 10,000 deaths. As railroad and telephone links are cut and airports are damaged, the lack of supply lines for rescue and recovery is another secondary consequence (a major problem following both the Haiti and Kashmir earthquakes).

How people cope and how quickly they can get back on their feet largely depends on whether the earthquake occurs in a high income country, where there are contingency plans for all stages of the hazard management cycle underpinned by financial support mainly from within the country. In low income countries there are fewer resources for rescue and recovery, and a reliance on international aid.

Exam tip

Always keep up to date. April 2016 had two serious earthquakes, in Ecuador and Japan. Both will make interesting research.

The secondary effects have both social and economic consequences. Many factories and offices are so damaged that work cannot resume for some considerable time, costing money in wages, lost production, future orders and exports. The community might also be threatened by hunger and disease and possibly by social disorder from looting etc. as people desperately seek to survive.

In rural areas, farmland and crops will be seriously affected if drainage or irrigation systems are disrupted and fields covered in rubble. Where landslides have blocked roads, farmers are not able to get their products to market. On the other hand, in urban areas the effects can be extremely severe because of the high density of buildings and the high value of the infrastructure. If buildings are completely destroyed, leaving large areas of derelict land, uncollected refuse and decomposing organic material can result in infestations of rats and flies. The Tohoku earthquake of 2010 had exceptionally severe secondary effects as a result of the 'triple whammy' of earthquake, tsunami and the resultant nuclear disaster.

Summary

- Earthquake characteristics include a focus, epicentre, depth and different types of waves (P, S, L and R waves).
- Earthquakes result from movement along fractures or faults in rocks and create different types of hazards including ground shaking (intensity and duration), liquefaction, landslides, avalanches and tsunamis.
- Demographic, economic and social impacts of earthquakes result from both primary and secondary causes.
- Earthquakes affect people and property and have impacts at global, regional and local scales.
- You will need to learn one (AS) or two (A-level) examples of an earthquake to demonstrate the varied degree of risk and impacts of earthquake activity.

Human factors affecting risk and vulnerability

Disaster versus hazard

A disaster is the realisation of a hazard 'which causes a significant impact on a vulnerable population'. While the terms 'hazard' and 'disaster' are often used casually or synonymously, there is a major distinction between them, which is shown clearly by the Degg model (Figure 40).

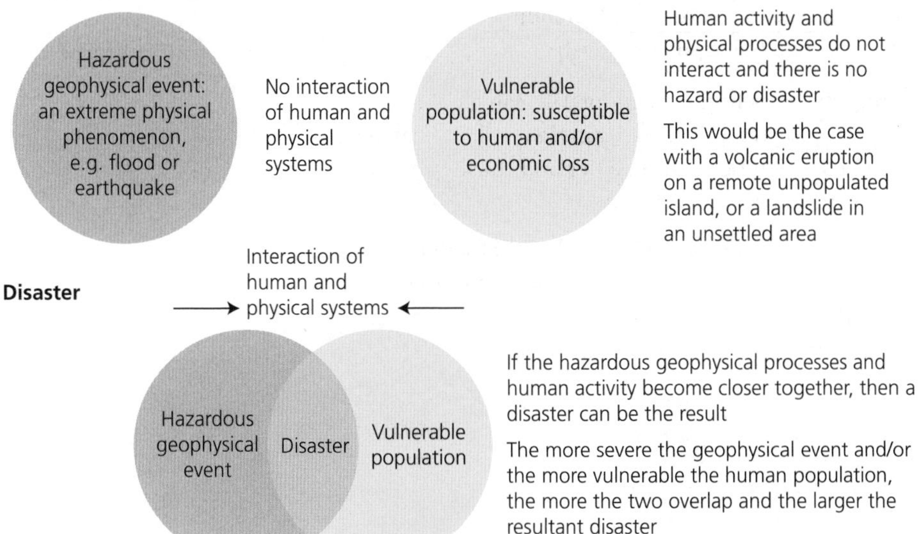

Figure 40 The Degg model

Risk

Risk is defined as 'the probability of a hazard occurring and creating loss of lives and livelihoods'. It might be assumed that risk of exposure to tectonic hazards is involuntary, but in reality people consciously place themselves at risk for a variety of reasons, including:

- the unpredictability of hazards: areas may not have experienced a hazard in living memory
- the changing risk over time (e.g. a perceived extinct volcano)
- lack of alternative locations to live, especially for the poor
- an assessment that economic benefits outweigh the costs, e.g. for areas of rich volcanic soils or of great tourism potential
- optimistic perceptions of hazard risks: it can all be solved by the technofix, or it won't happen to me

The risk is altered by human conditions and actions, for example two similar-magnitude earthquakes (Lomo Prieta, California and Bam, Iran) had very different consequences because the people in Bam (poorer in a developing country) were generally at much greater risk, i.e. they were more **vulnerable**.

Knowledge check 41

Choose three examples of tectonic hazard events where people have exacerbated the scale of the disaster by putting themselves at risk.

Vulnerability

Vulnerability implies a high risk of exposure to hazard, combined with an inability to cope. In human terms this is the degree of resistance offered by a social system to the impact of a hazardous event. This depends on the **resilience** of individuals and communities, the reliability of management systems and the quality of governance that have been put in place.

Certain conditions amplify vulnerability.

The risk equation

The risk equation measures the level of hazard risk for an area:

$$\text{risk} = \frac{\text{frequency and/or magnitude of hazard} \times \text{level of vulnerability}}{\text{capacity of population to cope (i.e. resilience level)}}$$

While the **intrinsic** physical properties of a hazard event profile can lay the foundations for the development of a disaster, it is the **extrinsic** areal or local factors that impact on the vulnerability of communities and societies and cause tectonic disasters. It is also to do with the actual communities and societies themselves.

The PAR model (Figure 41) helps to explain the variability in levels of vulnerability and resistance. It is this vulnerability (both human and economic) not the tectonic environment that helps to explain the differences in the severity of the social and economic impacts of physically similar hazard events (see Table 16).

Knowledge check 42

Explain how unsustainable development can increase the risk equation.

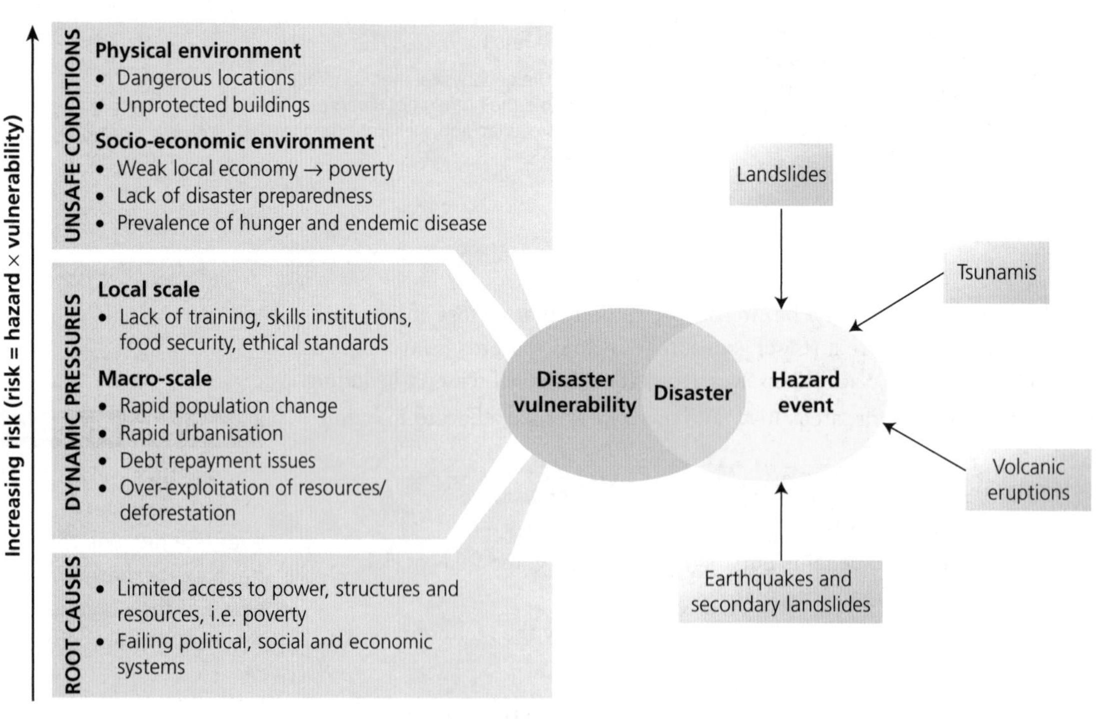

Figure 41 The PAR (pressure and release) model

Table 16 Differences in the severity of social and economic impacts of physically similar hazard events

		Magnitude	Fatalities	Damage US$ millions
1992	Erzican, Turkey	6.8	540	3,000
1999	Izmit, Turkey	7.4	17,225	12,000
1989	Loma Prieta, USA	7.1	68	10,000
1994	Northridge, USA	6.8	61	44,000

As the PAR model shows, certain drivers of disaster (root causes) result in pressures that create potentially unsafe conditions. The development paradigm argues that, at a macro-scale, the root causes of vulnerability lie in the contrasting economic and political systems of the developed/developing divide. The most vulnerable people are channelled into the most hazardous environments (the result of chronic malnutrition, disease, armed conflict, chaotic and ineffective governance, lack of educational empowerment). Therefore the risk equation is being increased because levels of vulnerability are increasing and resilience is decreasing.

Drivers of disaster and vulnerability

Economic factors

Human vulnerability is closely associated with levels of absolute poverty and the economic gap between rich and poor (inequality). Disasters are exacerbated by poverty (Haiti, Kashmir etc.). The poorest least developed countries (LDCs) lack money to invest in education, social services, basic infrastructure and technology, all of which help communities overcome disasters. Poor countries lack effective infrastructure. Economic growth increases economic assets and therefore raises risk unless managed effectively. However, developed countries can invest in technology for disaster reduction and production, and in aid after the hazard event.

Technological factors

While community preparedness and education can prove vital in mitigating disasters, technological solutions can play a major role, especially in building design and prevention and protection and also in the design of monitoring equipment (see pp. 89–92).

Social factors

World population is growing, especially in developing nations where there are higher levels of urbanisation and many people live in dense concentrations in unsafe political settings. It is not only the density of a population but also the population profile (age, gender and levels of education) that are significant. An increasingly ageing population, as in China (Sichuan), increases vulnerability with problems of emergency evacuation and survival. Housing conditions and quality of building have a major impact on the scale of deaths and injuries. Essentially, disadvantaged people are more likely to die, suffer injury and psychological trauma during the recovery and reconstruction phase because they live in poorer housing which is not earthquake proof.

In the Sichuan and Kashmir earthquakes, badly built schools led to disproportionate deaths amongst the young.

Political factors

The lack of strong central government produces a weak organisational structure. Equally, a lack of financial institutions inhibits disaster mitigation and both emergency and post-disaster recovery. A good strong central government leads to highly efficient rescue (Chinese earthquake). Haiti is a classic case of the cumulative impacts of poor quality governance over many years.

Geographical factors

Geographical factors can be highly significant and case-study-specific, such as location (rural, urban, coast), degrees of isolation and time of day.

- Increasing urbanisation, with poorly sited squatter settlements, especially in mega cities, creates high hazard risk and exposure. These huge cities are vulnerable to post-earthquake fires (Kobe).
- Destruction of rural environments can result in disasters among rural populations, with a loss of food supplies and livelihoods (2015 Nepal Gorkha earthquake).
- Relief, rescue and recovery efforts are difficult in some areas (Kashmir, where isolation, the cold climate and frontier position complicated relief and recovery).
- The geography may lead to multi-hazard hotspots where the impacts of earthquakes, tsunamis or volcanic eruptions are amplified by impacts of other hazards.
- Timing of the first earthquake and aftershocks (e.g. Christchurch 2010–11 and Italy 2016–17) have a major effect, especially on social impacts such as deaths.

Knowledge check 43

Define the term 'multi-hazard hotspot'.

Summary

- Economic factors affecting risk and vulnerability include level of development, level of technology, inequality and poverty.
- Social factors include population density, population profile (age, gender), housing conditions, quality of building and levels of education.
- Political factors include the quality of governance and strength of central government.
- Geographical factors include rural–urban location, time of day and degree of isolation.

Responses to tectonic hazards

Monitoring, **predicting** and **warning** of tectonic hazards are examples of modifying people's **vulnerability** to the hazard — this also includes community preparedness and land use planning.

Prediction buys time to:

- warn people to evacuate
- prepare for a hazard event
- manage impacts more effectively
- help insurance companies assess risk
- prioritise government spending
- help decision makers carry out cost–benefit calculations of, for example, building expensive hi-tech systems

When?

- **Recurrence intervals** — an indication of longer-term risk
- **Seasonality** — climatic and geomorphic hazards may have seasonal patterns, e.g. Atlantic hurricanes occur from June to November
- **Timing** — the hardest to predict, both in the long term (e.g. winter gales) and the short term (e.g. time of hurricane)

Where?

- **Regional scale** — easy to predict, e.g. plate boundaries, 'tornado alley', drought zones
- **Local scale** — more difficult, except for fixed-point hazards, e.g. floods, volcanoes, coastal erosion
- Moving hazards — extremely difficult, e.g. hurricane tracking

What?

- **Type of hazard** — many areas can be affected by more than one hazard; purpose of forecast is to predict what type of hazard might occur
- **Magnitude of hazard** — important in anticipating impacts and managing a response
- **Primary vs secondary impacts** — some hazards have 'multiple' natures; earthquakes may cause liquefaction, volcanoes may cause lahars

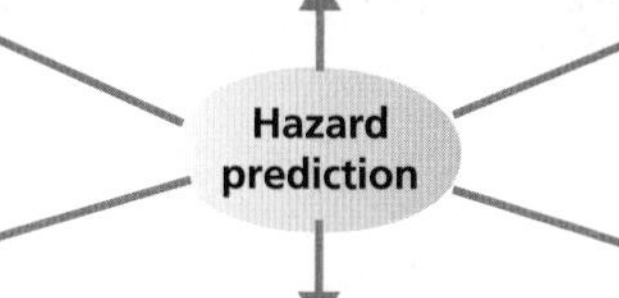

Why?

- **Reduce deaths** — by enabling evaluation
- **Reduce damage** — by enabling preparation
- **Enhance management** — by enabling cost–benefit calculations and risk assessment
- **Improve understanding** — by testing models against reality
- **Allow preparedness plans to be put in operation** — by individuals, local government, national agencies

Who?

- **Tell all?** — fair, but risks over-warning, scepticism and panic
- **Tell some?** — for example, emergency services, but may cause rumours and mistrust
- **Tell none?** — useful to test predictions, but difficult to justify

How?

- **Past records** — enable recurrence intervals to be estimated
- **Monitoring (physical)** — monitored and recorded using ground-based methods or, for climatic and volcanic hazards, remote sensing
- **Monitoring (human)** — factors influencing human vulnerability (e.g. incomes, exchange rates, unemployment); human impacts (e.g. deforestation)

Figure 42 The importance of hazard prediction

Monitoring, prediction and warning of earthquakes

Predicting earthquakes would allow people to evacuate the danger area before the event, but unfortunately this is only a seismologist's dream.

On a global scale, the regions of risk can be identified. At a **regional** scale, previous magnitude and frequency data can be used to pinpoint areas of risk and predict the **probabilities** of an earthquake occurring, but not precisely when this might happen. As an earthquake results from the release of strain building up in the crustal rocks, the areas which have 'loaded' for some time are likely to move in the future. Seismologists in California have produced earthquake probability maps for major fault lines such as San Andreas based on this '**gap theory**'.

At a local scale, attempts to predict earthquakes a few hours before the event are based on diaries of survivors (living histories) and the results from monitoring equipment. This includes changes in groundwater levels, release of radon gas or even (often used in China) unusual animal behaviour. These changes are thought to be due to ground dilation and rock cracking just before an earthquake. While the 1975 Heichang earthquake was successfully forecast 5½ hours before the event, allowing 90,000 people to be successfully evacuated, the Chinese failed to forecast the Great Tangshan earthquake of 1976 (an intra-plate earthquake), which was totally unexpected and resulted in a huge death toll.

Figure 43 shows a range of possible monitoring methods which could be used to explore earthquake processes.

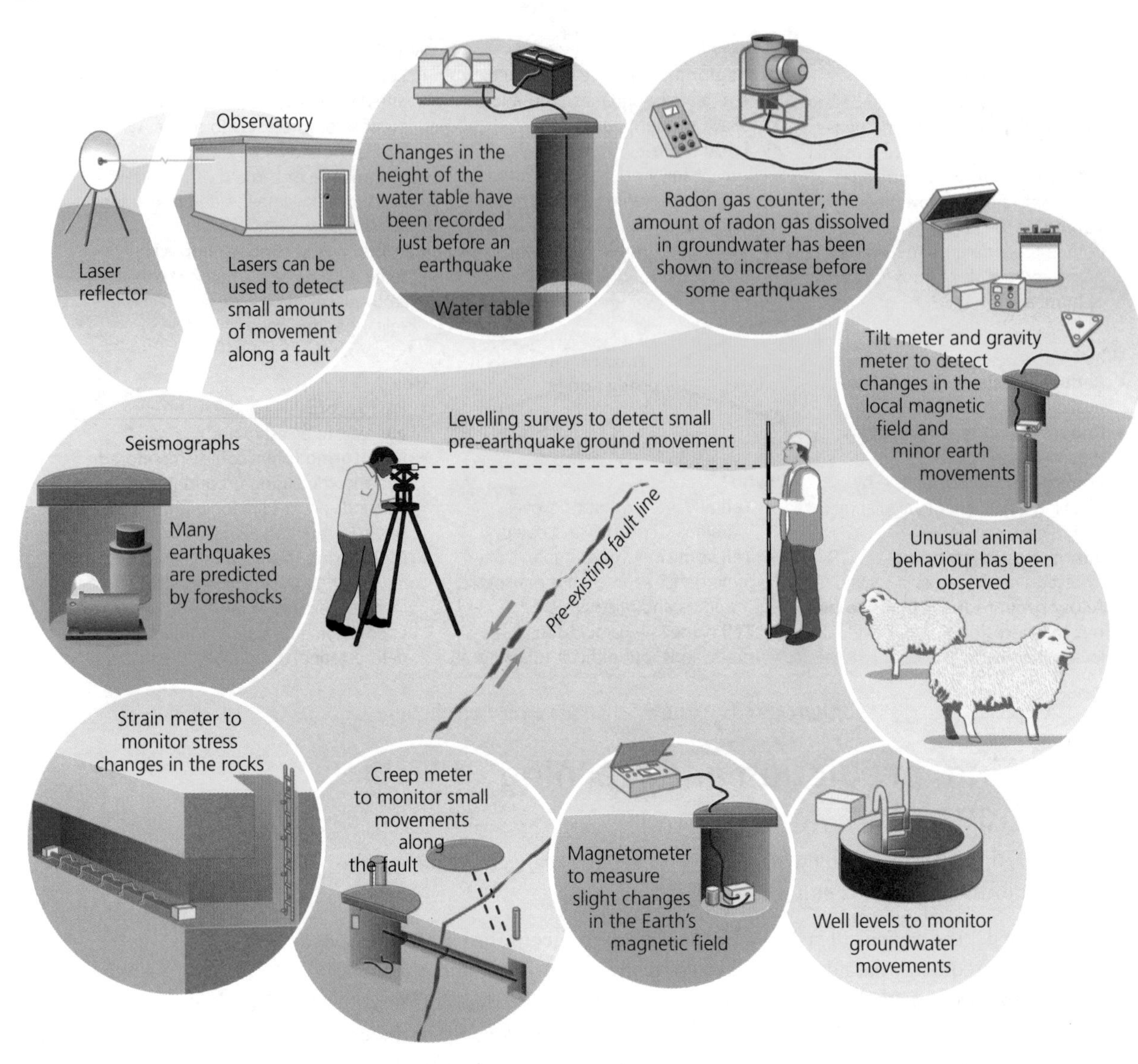

Figure 43 Monitoring methods for predicting an earthquake along an active fault line

It is possible to produce earthquake risk maps, which predict the likely impact of an earthquake on a particular designated area. These maps are based on known factors such as rock types, ground shaking, hill slopes, liquefaction danger and landslide potential. GIS are being used to develop this system further, especially by mapping concealed faults.

Monitoring, prediction and warning of volcanic eruptions

Given adequate monitoring, warning of certain volcanic eruptive phases is possible, making adaptive responses such as education, community preparation and emergency evacuation procedures feasible.

Most volcanic eruptions are preceded by a variety of environmental changes that accompany the rise of magma to the surface (i.e. precursors to an eruption).

Unfortunately, it is very difficult to predict the precise temporal occurrence of the actual eruption reaching danger levels. Moreover, for highly explosive eruptions, many of the phenomena are not present, and the precise timing of these eruptions is highly unpredictable.

1 **Earthquake activity** is common near volcanoes and, for predictive purposes, it is important to measure any increase in activity in relation to usual background levels. This requires an analysis of historic data plus supplementary field data from portable seismometers. Warning signs include a swarm of higher frequency earthquakes, reflecting the fracture of local rocks as magnetic pressure increases. Audible rumblings can sometimes be heard using sound instruments.
2 **Ground deformation** is sometimes the forerunner of an explosive eruption, although it can be difficult to measure for explosive subduction volcanoes. Tilt meters and other survey equipment are used to measure changes in slope. Electronic distance meters (EDM) can measure the distance between benchmarks placed on a volcano to pinpoint when the magma is rising and displacing the ground surface.
3 **Global positioning systems** (GPS) rely on satellites that orbit the Earth twice a day and constantly feed back information that allows the ground base to provide profiles. GPS receivers in the volcano can detect the build-up of pressure from rising magma.
4 **Thermal changes** occur as the magma rises to the surface and increases the surface temperature. Ground observations of hydrothermal phenomena, such as increased discharge from hot springs, increased steam from fumaroles, increases in temperature of crater lakes or hot springs, or wilting of vegetation on the volcanic slope, can be supplemented and confirmed by thermal imaging from satellites.
5 **Geochemical changes** can be detected in the composition of gases issuing from volcanic vents (increasing SO_2 or H_2S content). Direct field sampling of gases escaping from surface vents is the usual method, but remote sensing has been used too. SO_2 injected high into the atmosphere can be measured by onboard satellite equipment, and behaviour of volcanic plumes can be monitored by weather satellites.
6 **Lahars** have been monitored for years by local people but more recently videocams allow automatic detection systems. Seismometers detect ground vibrations from an approaching lahar, so an emergency message can be transmitted downslope to population centres, enabling short-term warnings and emergency evacuation.

Although there is no fully reliable forecasting and warning system, some success has been achieved in limiting deaths. For example, Phivolcs is a successful scheme developed in the Philippines to monitor the most active volcanoes in the most densely populated areas.

Once a volcano has erupted, for example the one in Montserrat, a danger zone is then delineated. Once clear warnings of new volanic activity are received, people are evacuated from the danger zone. The community is prepared in advance on evacuation routes and temporary food and shelter are supplied. However, the length of time available for evacuation is unpredictable, and sometimes there are false alarms. For example, in Montserrat, 5000 residents were evacuated three times between December 1995 and August 1996. In the Bay of Naples, home to Vesuvius, 700,000 people living in major cities such as Naples, are at risk from its eruption. Volcanologists and civil defence officials have drawn up an emergency evacuation plan. The operation is huge and even involves moving people to safety by ship with detailed routes carefully planned. Also, volcanic risk maps, using three grades of hazard risk, have to be created for a variety of hazards such as pyroclastic flows and ash falls. However, evacuation strategies, if managed effectively, can save thousands of lives.

Prediction and warning of tsunamis

Modifying the vulnerability is the main response to tsunamis. Scientists can predict a possible tsunami by monitoring earthquake activity, with the aim of issuing warnings to vulnerable populations who can evacuate the area. Tsunami forecasting and warning systems are well established in the Pacific, although frequent false alarms can lead to threat denial and financial loss.

Global-scale warning systems

In 1948 the Pacific Warning System for 24 Pacific Basin nations was established, with its centre near Honolulu in Hawaii. Seismic stations detect all the earthquakes and their events are interpreted to check for tsunami risk. The aim is to alert all areas at risk within 1 hour. The time it takes for a wave to travel across the Pacific allows ample time to warn shipping and evacuate low-lying coastal areas. As not all earthquakes result in tsunamis, it is a difficult decision whether to issue a warning. If the earthquake is larger than 7.5 (MMS) all locations within 3 hours' 'travel time' of the tsunami waves are put on warning alert to evacuate the coast, with areas 3–6 hours away put on standby.

There was no Indian Ocean Warning System in place for the 2004 Boxing Day tsunami, although one has subsequently been developed, based in Indonesia and India.

Regional-scale warning systems

Regional-scale warning systems aim to respond to locally generated tsunamis with short warning times as these pose a much greater threat. Ninety per cent of tsunamis occur within 400 km of the source area, so there may be less than 30 minutes between tsunami formation and landfall.

Japan has the most developed system — the target is to issue a warning within 20 minutes of the approach of a **tsunamigenic** earthquake within 600 km of the Japanese coastline. Such a warning was issued for the Tohoku earthquake of 2011, but the height of the tsunami wall failed to protect from the 40 m high waves. In 1994 a new detector and computer system was set up so that wave heights and arrival times could be more rapidly transmitted.

There are three main difficulties to overcome. First, the tsunami may destroy power and communication lines; second, as at Aceh, Indonesia in 2004, events many occur too quickly to issue a warning. Third, warnings must be supported by effective land-based evacuation routes and community education.

Mitigation and adaptation of tectonic hazards

A useful framework for classifying responses to tectonic hazards, developed by K. Smith, divides them into three categories:

1 modify the event
2 modify the vulnerability
3 modify the loss

Modify the event

While little can be done to control most volcanic hazards, some progress has been made in controlling lava flows. Seawater surges were successfully used to cool and solidify the lava flows during the 1973 Eldafell eruption in Iceland, and stop it advancing on the harbour of Vestmannaeyjar. Explosives have been used with some success on Mt Etna in Sicily to create artificial barriers to divert lava flows away from villages in the 1983, 1991 and 2001 eruptions.

Some attempts have been made to modify the impact of the tsunami hazard by hazard-resistant design. Defensive engineering works provide some protection, and the trend now is for a combination of hard engineering, using onshore walls for high value urban areas, and the redevelopment of natural protection provided by coral reefs and mangroves for rural areas.

Being able to control the physical variables of an earthquake, such as duration of shaking, is unlikely in the foreseeable future, although human-induced earthquakes such as those caused by dam construction or fracking could be prevented by not allowing development in areas subject to seismic hazards.

The main way of modifying an earthquake event is by **hazard-resistant building design** to develop **aseismic** (earthquake-resistant) buildings, as the collapse of buildings is responsible for the majority of deaths, injuries and economic losses. There is no clear relationship between building age and damage, although recent quakes have shown that specially designed, high-specification aseismic buildings in California and Japan do perform well even in high magnitude earthquakes.

There are currently three main types of building using the techno fix of expensive aseismic designs. These are ideal for important public buildings, key services such as hospitals and utilities such as power stations, but they are too expensive for homes. This is important as 70% of the world's 100 largest cities (12.5% of the world's population) are exposed to significant earthquake hazards once every 50 years.

Level of development is a key factor, as only economically developed nations can afford to **enforce** the strict seismic and building codes that can reduce death rates. In many developing or emerging nations there may be notional codes, but there is corruption and little money or political will to enforce them, hence the significant collapse of school buildings in the Sichuan earthquake. Recently, low-cost aseismic buildings suitable for rural and urban areas have been designed using cheap local materials such as wood and wattle and daub, and avoiding materials such as concrete lintels and corrugated iron, which cause death and injury.

Two problems with this approach are that (i) as in Christchurch, New Zealand, many older buildings need 'retrofitting' to bring them up to current higher standards of earthquake-resistant design, and (ii) damage is often from a variety of causes, not just shaking.

Modify the vulnerability

In addition to prediction, warning and monitoring other key parts of this strategy include land use planning and zoning, community preparedness and education.

Land use planning and layout is crucial in mitigating the severity of impacts of all three tectonic hazards.

- Tectonic hazard risk maps identify the most hazardous areas, which can be regulated by building codes. Lessons learned from **major earthquakes** are incorporated into planning new developments or rebuilding.
- Avoiding overly high density urban squatter settlements and providing public open space creates safe areas away from fires and aftershock damage. Considerable thought also needs to be given to the siting of public buildings, which should be preferably scattered in areas of low risk to reduce the chances of the total collapse of services (part of Tokyo planning).
- In areas of **volcanic hazard** risk maps are deployed (though few are available in developing countries). However, in areas such as Hawaii, lava flow hazards have been mapped and can be used as the basis for informed land use planning, avoiding valleys where flows are concentrated.
- In **tsunami-prone** areas, rezoning of low-lying coastal land can be an excellent defence. For example, in Crescent City, California, following tsunami damage from the 1964 Alaskan earthquake, the waterfront has been turned into public parks, and businesses moved to higher ground back from the shore.

Community preparedness and education are the core strategy of any programme to modify the vulnerability of people to tectonic hazard. Many volcanic events are preceded by clear warning of activity. Preparation of the community through education about precursors to look for, how to evacuate an area and how to develop resistance is key.

Community preparedness for seismic hazards is centred on preparing the general public to cope, and the emergency services and government to manage before, during and after the event. Experience as to how people behave in earthquakes has helped to devise recommendations for appropriate action and earthquake drills are now widely publicised.

Knowledge check 44

List the precursors communities should be made aware of.

In California, there is increased emphasis on using **smart technology** to prepare the emergency services.

Modify the loss

Essentially this has two major facets: **aid** and **insurance**. **Insurance** is mainly available in economically richer nations. The vast majority of people at risk from tectonic hazards do not have access to affordable insurance. It is largely commercial and industrial property that is insured against tectonic risk and disaster damage.

Insurance is a key strategy for economically developed countries. However, while individuals realise that the benefits of purchasing an insurance policy are enormous and could outweigh costs of damage, insurers who are wary of huge payouts following major hazard events assess the risk and charge accordingly. They also force householders to take preventative measures such as refitting their houses. Private properties become uninsurable in high risk areas and for poorer people, leading to governments taking over provision in some instances.

Humanitarian concern for disaster victims results in **emergency aid** flowing in from governments, NGOs and private donations. Aid is used at all stages of the hazard management cycle (see Figure 44) for relief, rehabilitation and reconstruction.

Exam tip

Useful case studies for this section include Haiti 2010, Nepal 2015 and the successes and failures of international aid following the Boxing Day tsunami in 2004.

Short-term and long-term responses to the effects of earthquake and volcanic hazards

There are two useful frameworks that can be used to look at responses over time.

1 The **Hazard Disaster Management Cycle** (Figure 44) identifies a number of phases in the management of a hazard from immediate response, through rehabilitation, to recovery and the development of resilience via mitigation strategies. Various versions of the cycle show how the strategies of modify the loss, modify the event and modify human vulnerability fit in the cycle. Today technology is of increasing importance in the management of all stages of the cycle.

Knowledge check 45

Define the following terms: 'resilience', 'recovery', 'rehabilitation'.

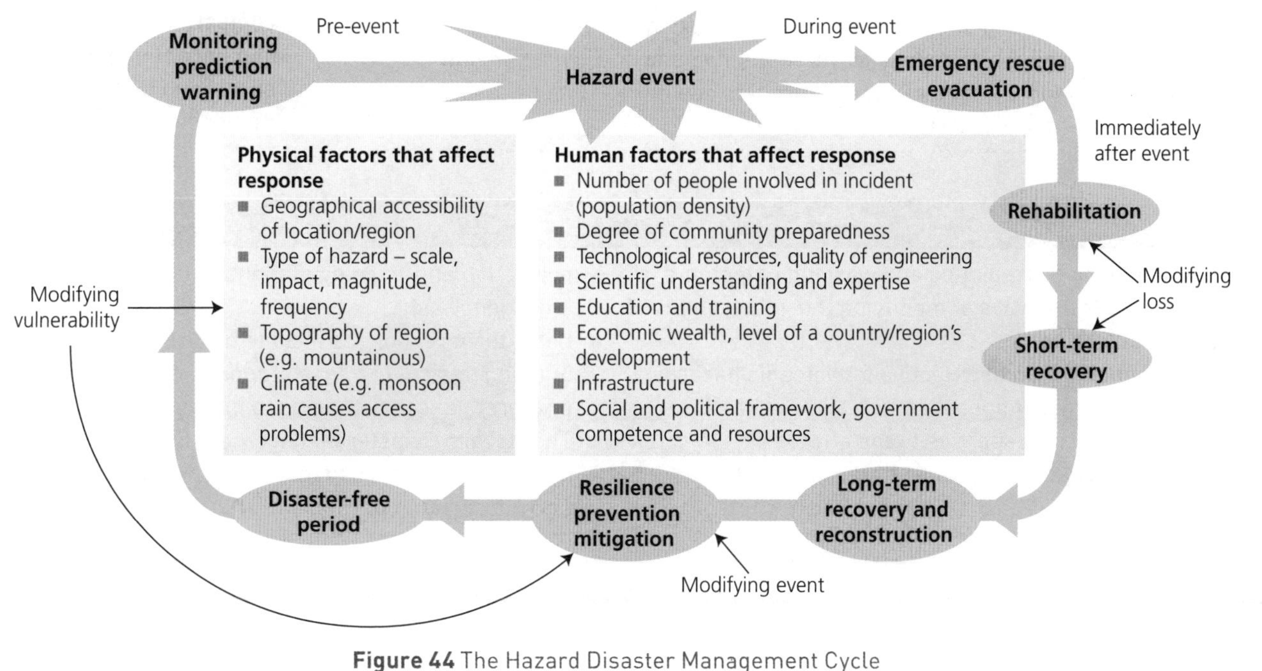

Figure 44 The Hazard Disaster Management Cycle

2 **Park's disaster-response curve** (Figure 45) allows modelling of the impact of a disaster from pre-disaster, through the impact, to post-disaster recovery, and shows the importance of various strategies over the lifecycle of a hazard event.

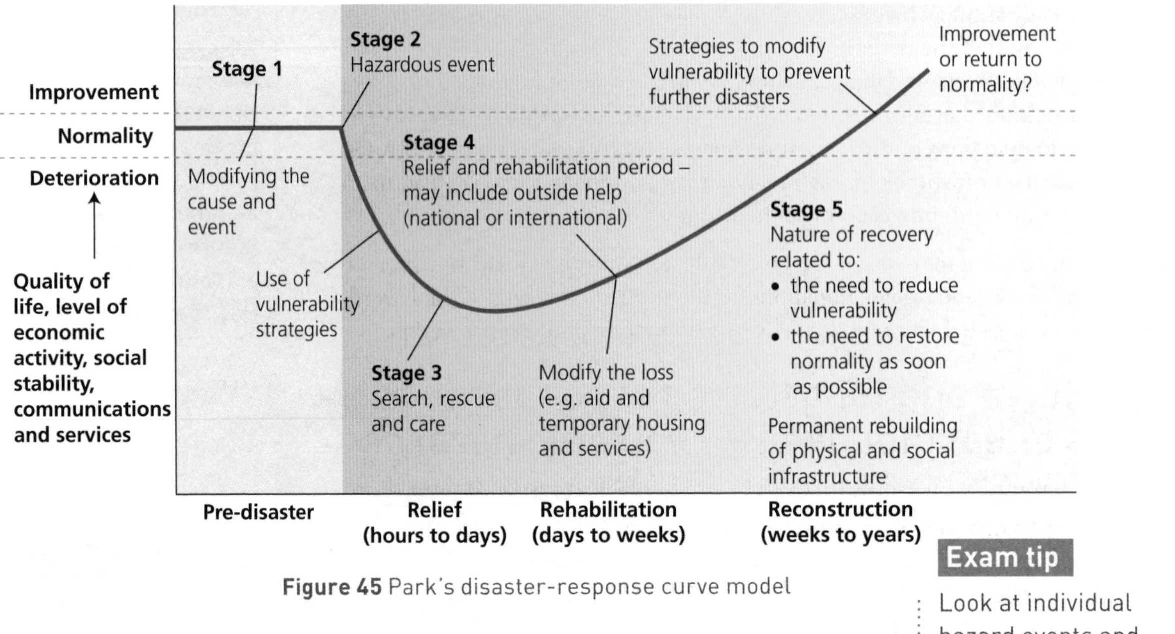

Figure 45 Park's disaster-response curve model

Exam tip

Look at individual hazard events and devise 'tailor made' diagrams for your chosen events to compare the progress and impact of both short- and long-term responses.

Exam tip

To keep your case studies up to date use the internet — there are often many twists and turns. You can look at the Boxing Day tsunami 10 years on. Use Google Earth to look at the rebuilding and see if you can still see the damage. Or you can look at Haiti to see if there has been any progress — there are conflicting accounts.

Summary

- Monitoring, predicting and warning of tectonic hazards are ways of modifying the vulnerability of populations.
- Prediction can be effective for volcanic hazards but is almost impossible for earthquakes.
- Short-term responses to the effects of earthquake and volcanic hazards include prediction and warning, national and international emergency aid.
- Long-term responses include hazard-resistant building design, land use planning, community preparedness, education and insurance.
- The Hazard Disaster Management Cycle shows how the choice of response depends on complex and interrelated physical and human factors.

Questions & Answers

About this section

The questions below are typical of the style and structure that you can expect to see in the exam papers. For the AS questions, the number of lines given in the exam answer booklet is an indication of the level of detail required.

There are comments on each question, preceded by ⓔ, which offer guidance on question interpretation. Student responses are then provided, with detailed comments for each answer, preceded by ⓔ, indicating the strengths and weaknesses of the answer and the number of marks that would be awarded.

The examiners have a grid which gives them the maximum marks for each Assessment Objective (AO). The mark scheme includes indicative content, marking guidance and, for marks totals in excess of 5, marks bands.

Glaciated landscapes

ⓔ The first two questions are in the style of WJEC AS questions. They have some shorter definitions or data response questions marked by points marking and longer questions marked using the 'band' system of marking. For the longer 15 mark answers you are required to develop a sustained line of reasoning that is coherent, relevant, substantiated and logically structured.

Question 1 (WJEC AS style)

(a) Define the equilibrium point of a glacier. (3 marks AO1)

ⓔ 1 mark is awarded for the basic point and then up to 2 further marks for further development and amplification in a logical sequence.

Student answer

The equilibrium point of a glacier is where accumulation and ablation balance each other out ✓, where losses from ablation by melting ✓ are balanced by gains from accumulation of fresh snow and ice from above ✓ so at this point, which will vary both spatially and temporally ✓, inputs are equal to outputs. There is more accumulation in the upper part and more ablation lower down.

ⓔ This answer scores 3 marks with ease.

(b) (i) Explain how the glacier budget works as a system. (5 marks AO1)

ⓔ This is a good example of a question that requires a simple diagram of a glacial budget — a diagram showing inputs and outputs is so much clearer than words and is simple to draw.

Student answer

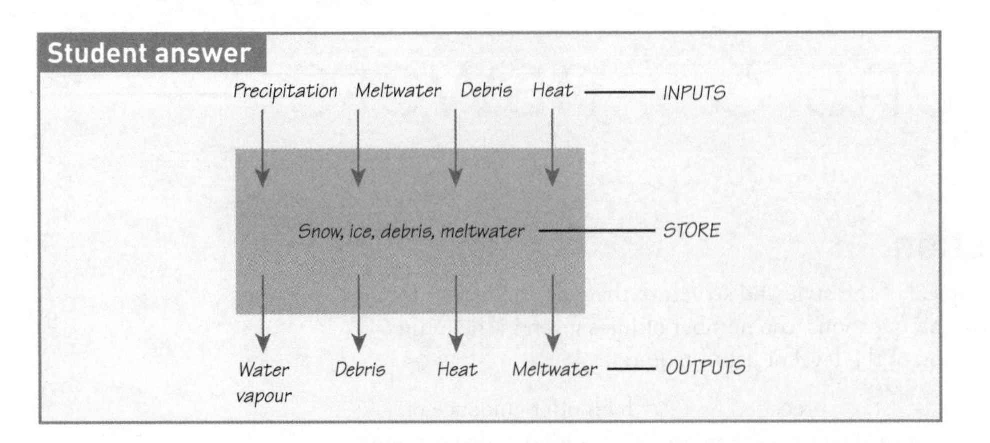

ⓔ The diagram is sound but to score full marks a written explanation is needed to explain the idea of a budget. This answer would score 3 marks.

Indicative content:

- A system consists of inputs, outputs and the balance between them by various flows affecting the size of the store (glacier).
- The glacier budget is driven by inputs of energy from the sun, which evaporates water from the oceans to create air masses, which produce snowfall and other precipitation (i.e. accumulation).
- Potential energy is expended as the glacier flows downwards under the influence of gravity.
- Where accumulation is greater than ablation a positive budget or mass balance occurs.
- Where ablation is greater than accumulation a negative balance occurs.
- Mass balance is defined as the gains by accumulation and losses by ablation, which determine the size of the glacier, with annual and longer-term variations.
- Ablation occurs in the lower regions of the glacier, resulting from sublimation, calving and meltwater.

(b) (ii) Describe and explain the importance of positive and negative feedback in influencing the glacier budget. (5 marks AO1, 3 marks AO2)

ⓔ Feedback is a complex concept and a key word to understand. Always have some examples to support your arguments and preferably statistics too.

Using the concept of negative feedback, try to explain the factors that could decrease the impact of global warming by the process of global dimming.

Another example to understand is how the THC could be disrupted by changes in the Arctic ice and block off the impact of the Gulf Stream, so causing cooling in northern Europe despite global warming overall.

Student answer

Feedback effects are those that can either amplify a change and make it larger (positive feedback) or diminish the change and make it smaller (negative feedback). Positive feedback can occur when the snow and ice cover increases, raising albedo and leading to more cooling and more snowfall and ice cover, so accelerating the increase in size of glacier stores. The melting of the snow and ice decreases albedo, but methane is emitted from melting permafrost so climate warming accelerates, leading to more cooling and accelerating loss of ice sheet cover, so quickening the decrease in glacier size. Negative feedback can decrease the rate of warming, or cooling when looking at climate change, which has a knock-on effect on ice masses.

e This answer is worth only 2 marks for AO1 as it lacks definition. It shows good understanding for 3 AO2 marks. Overall: 5 marks.

Question 2 (WJEC AS style)

(a) (i) Define a cirque (corrie/cwm). (2 marks AO1)

e A simple, developed definition is required. Credit appropriate exemplar for 1 mark.

Student answer

A cirque is an armchair-shaped hollow on a hillside at high altitudes, usually above a glaciated valley ✓. It forms initially from a nivation hollow that is then enlarged by freeze–thaw weathering ✓.

e This answer scores 1 mark for a basic definition and 1 mark for development.

Study the table.

Altitude (m) (at base or lake)	Orientation	Width at widest point (m)	Approximate back wall height (m)
690	NNE	500	200
710	NNE	800	210
700	NNE	900	260
760	ENE	100	160
920	NNW	600	150
950	WNW	600	160
720	NE	900	270
760	NE	800	170
950	ESE	900	160
960	E	500	200

(a) (ii) Explain two ways you could use statistical and/or graphical methods to analyse the information shown in the table. (2 × 2 marks AO3)

e Note that there are many feasible answers. Reward 2 marks for each of two — one for naming the method and one for amplification for information shown.

Student answer

You could use a rose diagram to show the altitude of the corries and you could create a histogram to show how many corries are orientated in each direction.

ⓔ **1 mark awarded.** Naming the rose diagram is not enough for a mark — a rose diagram would not be suitable for altitude, so 0 marks; 1 mark credit *could* be given for 'histogram' but again it is not a useful technique for orientation and it is not explained.

Indicative content:

Graphical methods could include:

- A rose diagram could be used to show corrie orientation.
- A regression line could be used to correlate corrie size (height of back wall) with height of corrie basin.
- A rose diagram could relate corrie orientation to altitude.
- A frequency dispersion diagram or histogram could show the percentage orientation of a group of corries.

Statistical methods of analysis could include:

- Correlation using Spearman rank (r_s) of a number of features such as size with height or aspect.

(b) Assess the features that might influence corrie size and aspect. (4 marks AO1, 3 marks AO2)

ⓔ AO1 involves knowledge and understanding of the factors influencing corrie size and corrie aspect.

Indicative content:

AO1

- Corrie size can be defined in a number of ways, such as height of back wall, area in km^2 excavated (multiply length by breadth).
- Corrie size is dependent on geology and how easily it can be eroded, for example evidence of jointing will encourage freeze–thaw.
- It can also be influenced by aspect or orientation, i.e. which way the corrie faces.
- When incipient corries form, the snow collects most easily on sheltered (from prevailing southwesterly winds) north- and east-facing slopes as it is not blown away.
- North- and east-facing slopes in the northern hemisphere are shady so there is less snow melt and maximum snow patch erosion.
- Height and elevation is also important as the higher the altitude the more likely snow will compact into ice.

AO2

This involves an assessment of the importance of factors, preferably exemplified locations you have researched.

In theory, the most common aspect should be northeast-facing where corries should be larger and develop at a lower altitude. In reality, there are always anomalies such as low-height corries on a south-facing slope.

Geology is an important local factor. In a survey of the Glyders, structure and lithology were seen to exert geological controls so virtually all of the corries face towards the northeast with none in any other orientation.

Student answer

Corrie size is influenced by its mode of formation. The formation of a corrie (cirque) begins with a snow patch ✓. The erosion of which enlarges the hollow ✓. The combination of freeze–thaw and plucking steepens the headwall. This freeze–thaw takes place down the bergschrund. The hollow is enlarged in size by the rotational movement of the corrie glacier and this hollow is deepened and enlarged by abrasion from all the loose debris which collects at the base of the corrie glacier. This explains how the corrie is enlarged to become a large size.

When the cirques are free of glacier ice they often contain small lakes or tarns held back by a rock bar covered with moraine at the mouth of the corrie. An example of a corrie is Red Tarn, Helvellyn which faces northeast, the most common aspect for corries ✓ as this is where most snow can collect.

e **2/7 marks awarded.** This does not really answer the question set as factors are poorly identified. It is a reasonable account as to how the corrie forms. Size and aspect are both mentioned but there is limited attempt to apply the knowledge and understanding to the question. The last paragraph is irrelevant. Band 2 for AO1 and no attempt at assessment for AO2, so no marks. This is an example where a student has not applied knowledge and understanding to the question set, so only 2 marks is disappointing.

The next question is in the format of Eduqas AS and requires extended writing, with the ability to develop a sustained line of argument.

Question 3 (Eduqas AS style)

Analyse the view that periglacial processes form distinctive landforms which contribute to a unique environment. (10 marks AO1, 10 marks AO2)

e This question requires you to demonstrate your ability to develop a sustained line of reasoning, which is coherent, relevant, substantiated and logically structured. In this case, is the periglacial environment a unique process environment as a result of a suite of distinctive landforms or does it contain many landforms which are found elsewhere?

You have to go from process to landform to landscape in a logical answer in order to earn maximum marks.

Indicative content:

Half the marks are for knowledge and understanding of how physical processes create landforms (AO1).

- Features of periglacial environments include intense frosts during winter, highest average annual temperatures range from 1°C to −4°C, low precipitation (less than 100 mm in winter, less than 500 mm in summer), frequent cycles of freezing and thawing.

- Periglacial processes include: freeze–thaw leading to frost shattering, ice wedging and frost heaving, ice segregation and formation of ice lenses as well as mass movement by solifluction.
- Landforms include:
  - unique ground ice features:
    - ice wedge polygons on valley floors
    - patterned ground resulting from frost heaving
    - pingos and palsas from formation of ice cores
  - frost shattering:
    - block fields, tors, scree slopes etc. The process is not unique, but it occurs with greater severity in periglacial environments
  - the role of mass movement which forms solifluction features associated with permafrost areas
  - the role of snow and the formation of nivation hollows
  - the role of wind and meltwater rivers to produce loess and anastomosing damage (not unique to periglacial environments)

For the remaining 50% of marks you have to demonstrate application of knowledge and understanding through an analysis of unique the landforms are to periglacial areas and whether they collectively form a distinctive assemblage that is typical of periglacial areas only (A02).

- Analysis of the characteristic processes 1 to 5 and whether they do or do not produce distinctive landforms.
- Analysis (preferably with block diagram to show the downslope catena of features) as to whether there is a typical assemblage which forms a unique landscape (as a process environment).
- Analysis of interdependence of processes in periglacial areas.
- Analysis of non-unique features.
- Analysis of whether relict periglacial areas contain features of periglacial areas therefore reinforcing the concept of distinctiveness.

Student answer

Cold climate environments develop distinctive geomorphology because of four basic processes.

The 9% expansion of water on freezing leads to frost shattering which forms block fields and screes and tors.

The contraction and cracking of rapidly freezing ground in which ice wedges form and frost heaving takes place leading to patterned ground.

The migration of subsurface water to freezing front by suction leads to the formation of ice lens and subsequently pingos and pulsars.

The mass movement of the 'top' active layer over the permafrost downslope largely by solifluction leads to lobes, head deposits and terraces.

Only frost shattering is not an exclusive process as it does occur outside periglacial areas whereas the other three processes are associated with the permanently frozen ground (permafrost) which is a key feature of periglacial areas.

Periglacial climates, which cause permafrost as in Scotland or northern Canada, typically have the following features:

- intense winter frosts, during winter and on any snow-free ground in summer
- high average annual temperatures between 1°C and –4°C
- daily below 0°C for at least nine months and below –10°C for at least 10 months of the year
- temperatures fluctuating through frequent freeze–thaw cycles to cause interstitial ice in any cracks to melt from time to time

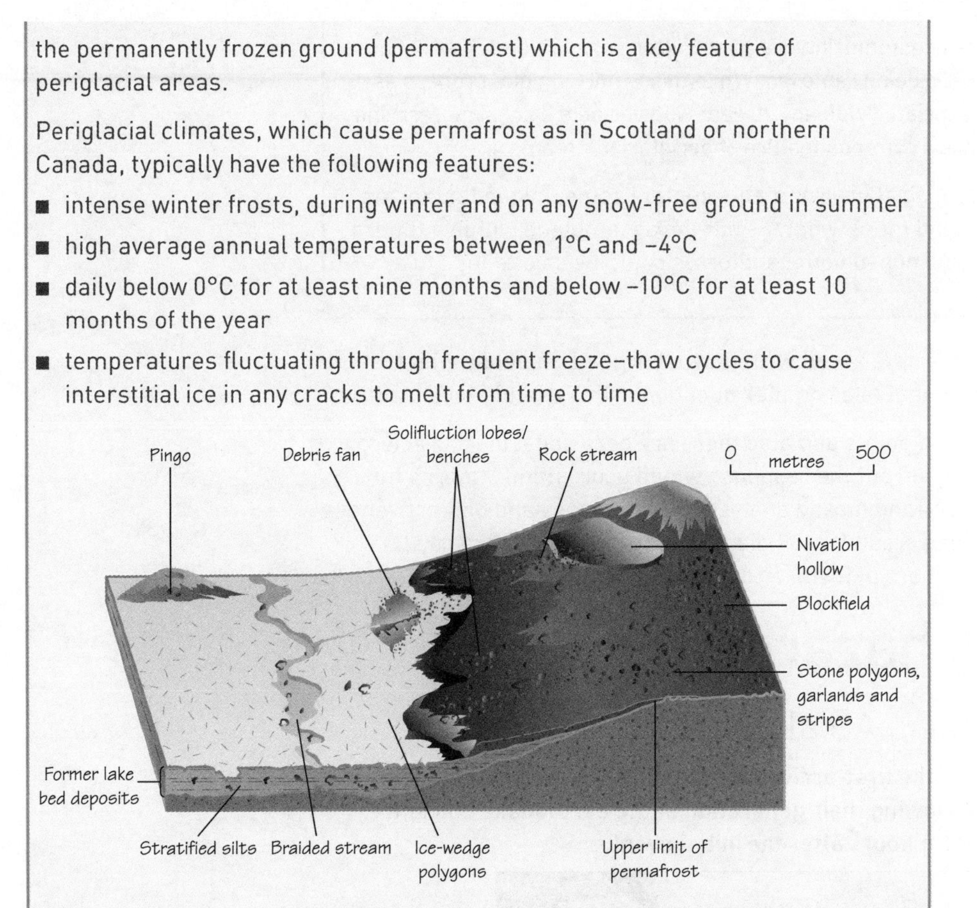

My drawing shows a typical periglacial landscape from high-altitude areas down to the valley bottom. It is the arrangement of the features shown which compose the typical periglacial landscape — which is distinctive and can be seen not only in present-day environments but also as relict landscape from the Pleistocene as in southern Britain, which was beyond the margin of the maximum Devensian glaciation and is therefore a periglacial area.

Of the individual elements, some are unique to periglacial areas such as the pingos (ice cone mass mound 50 m high) and the patterned ground which includes circles, polygons and stripes — formed by frost heaving from downslope solifluction whereby circles are elongated into stripes. Other features such as the block fields and residual tors (e.g. Stiperstones) are not unique to periglacial areas, but they are a common feature on hill tops and plateaux within them.

Other features are formed by processes which occur more widely — for example, nivation or snow patch erosion leads to the formation of hollows at the base of a slope, and this process can occur outside periglacial areas.

Many periglacial areas are characterised by extreme aridity (physiological drought), only around 500 mm of rainfall, largely frozen leading to an absence of vegetation. As in standard desert areas, out-blowing winds from high pressure zones remove the silt to create loess. Water erosion in periglacial areas is inevitably highly seasonal, especially occurring in late spring and early summer when surface snow and ice and the active layer melt. The anastomosing drainage pattern of a braided river because of the high amount of debris being removed. While this is not a unique process as it is a type of drainage associated with any stream with variable discharge carrying large amounts of load, it is a common feature of periglacial streams.

In conclusion, these periglacial environments contain some unique landforms and some that can be found more widely — but the assemblage within a tundra slope catena of unique and non-unique landforms could be said to lead to a distinctive landscape.

e 19/20 marks awarded This is a well written, well argued response which provides a sustained argument to a complex question with a useful block diagram.

It is advisable to avoid bullet points and also there are occasional inaccuracies, e.g. pulsars instead of palsas, but the response would score Band 3 marks for both knowledge and understanding and analysis of uniqueness and distinctiveness would be considered (giving credit for the diagram) for 9 + 10 (19–20 marks). Perhaps a few more exemplars of features could be included for 10 for AO1.

Tectonic hazards

Question 1 (Eduqas AS style)

(a) The map below shows the first-arrival travel times of waves in the Boxing Day 2004 tsunami, following their generation at the earthquake epicentre. The numbers represent hours after the initial event.

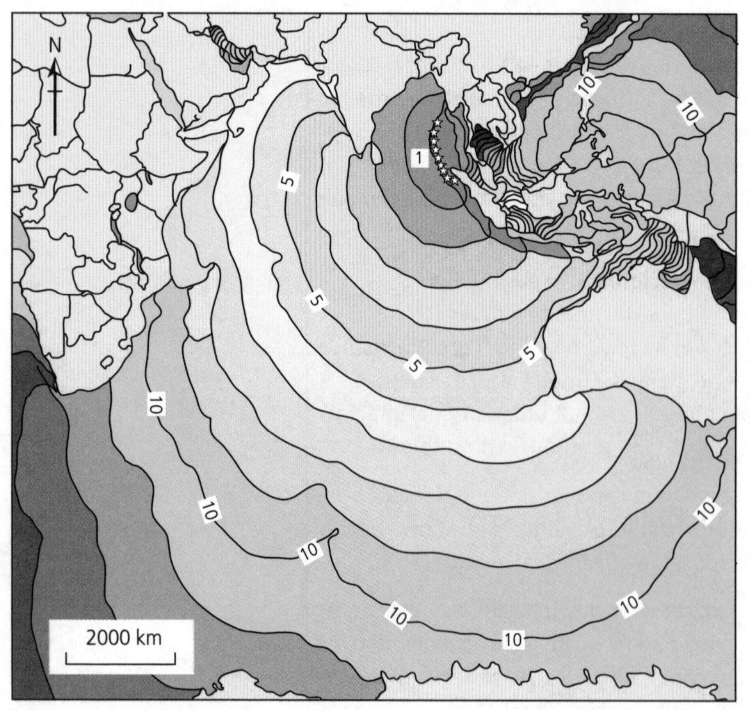

Progress of the Boxing Day 2004 tsunami across the Indian Ocean

(i) Study the map. Describe the temporal impact of this event across the Indian Ocean. (6 marks AO3)

ⓔ This question follows the format of Eduqas AS questions. This is a skills-based question so it relies on your accurate interpretation of the map.

Student answer

The zone of fault rupture (epicentre) was from the Sumatra earthquake at the Sunda trench giving no warning to Aceh in Indonesia ✓. After 2 hours the wave had spread to Sri Lanka and southern Sumatra and Thailand ✓. Progress was much more rapid across the open waters of the Indian Ocean than to Java and northern Sumatra ✓. After 5 hours impacts had spread to the west coast of India and northwest Australia ✓. By 7–8 hours the waves had reached to the Somali coast and the southern Australia coast ✓. It is noteworthy that places such as Borneo and Brunei, much nearer, were reached at the same time as Antarctica ✓. The last places to feel the impact, some 24 hours later, included the Gulf of Thailand and northeast Australia — so there is not a clear correlation to distance ✓. Coastal configuration is clearly important as well as the degree of open water for the wave to move across ✓.

ⓔ The marks are awarded in three bands based on the detail of description and the thoroughness of resource use.

Band 3: 5–6 marks

Band 2: 3–4 marks

Band 1: 1–2 marks

This answer achieves the maximum 6 marks for accurate analysis of the resource.

(a) (ii) Look at the table below. Suggest and justify a statistical technique you could use to correlate the arrival time of the tsunami with the number of deaths. (4 marks)

Human impacts of the Boxing Day tsunami

	Indonesia	Burma (Myanmar)	India	Maldives	Sri Lanka	Thailand
Deaths	169,000	81	10,750	81	31,000	5,300 (including 2,248 foreign nationals)
Missing	150,000+	1	5,550	n/a	4,000	2,800
Homes damaged or destroyed	200,100	5,000	15,000	15,000	100,000	60,000+
People displaced (some in relief camps)	600,000	10,000–15,000	140,000	11,500	500,000	300,000 (Burmese migrants a real problem)
Total population	217,500,000	48,956,000	1,041,410,000	309,000	19,287,000	64,340,000

Source: Geo Factsheet Number 194, www.curriculum-press.co.uk

ⓔ Try out the technique to see whether it works.

Student answer

An ideal correlation technique is Spearman's rank (r_s) ✓.

$$r_s = [1 - \frac{6\Sigma D^2}{N^3} - N]$$

However, it would be necessary to obtain more information of deaths, perhaps adding four more sites such as Somali Republic Kenya, Andaman Islands, Malaysia etc., as ten items are needed for reliability and the table shows only six ✓.

Data by country, for example India and Indonesia, also would need modifying as the tsunami hit various coasts at different times. The table needs to be used once the correlation has been calculated ✓ to ascertain whether the critical value has been exceeded and at what confidence level ✓.

ⓔ This answer scores the maximum 4 marks because the choice of technique is well justified.

(b) Study the table.

(i) Calculate which country had the highest percentage of deaths out of the total number of deaths (estimated at 275,000). (2 marks AO3)

ⓔ For a calculation always show your working, because although you may get the wrong answer through a simple error, you will get marks for the method.

Answer is Indonesia.

$$\frac{169{,}000}{275{,}000} \times 100 = 61\% \checkmark$$

(b) (ii) Suggest possible reasons for this. (4 marks)

The earthquake was MM 9 ✓and the arrival of a very high tsunami was instantaneous with no chance to prepare for its onset in places such as Aceh as it occurred in shallow water offshore. Aceh was a poor, war torn province of Indonesia — with such huge damage to housing etc., this was bound to result in huge numbers of deaths ✓. It was possible that there was poor governance and little education and community preparedness in Indonesia, so the tsunami had maximum impact ✓.

ⓔ The maximum 4 marks are awarded for the correct calculation and good reasoning shown. There are many more alternative answers that you could develop based on your understanding of factors influencing disaster impact.

(b) (iii) Select and justify cartographical techniques you might use to show information on deaths and housing damage. (4 marks)

Cartographical techniques could include proportional located symbols (circles, squares, bars of selected statistics superimposed on a base map) ✓; pie or bar graphs of selected statistics superimposed on a base map. These could be drawn to show a proportion of the total ✓. Both of these would best be shown using located data ✓. Choropleth maps could be used but are not especially suitable ✓.

ⓔ Answers that score well will select and justify through evaluation. The data must be easily read and interpreted and be able to be compared from country to country. For maximum marks, both deaths and homes destroyed should be covered and techniques well selected and justified. This answer shows some ideas but they are too generalised and not linked well to the data, so 2 marks only are awarded.

(c) Using the map on p. 104, the table on p.105 and your own knowledge, analyse the appropriateness of possible long- and short-term responses to manage and mitigate the impacts of tsunamis. (12 marks: 5 marks AO1, 7 marks AO2)

ⓔ This is a wide-ranging question. One way to structure your answer is to use a framework such as the Hazard Management Cycle or Park's response curve to include the temporal scale of short-term and long-term management. The question also includes 'mitigate' and 'manage' so clearly you have to consider both.

AO1 content encompasses knowledge and understanding of short-term responses which occur immediately after the tsunami in the rescue period and during the first weeks of recovery, whereas long-term responses occur as a result of planning and development in the rehabilitation period, normally up to 20 years after the event.

Mitigation may include some protection and monitoring strategies which are part of the overall management process.

For AO2 you need to demonstrate the application of knowledge and understanding through an analysis of the appropriateness of the responses, e.g. did they work and was money well spent so that mitigation and management would improve in future disasters. You should give context as required, for example, Chile, Boxing Day (Asia), Solomon Islands or Tohoku (Japan).

High-scoring responses will consider:

- whether the efforts were well managed by governments, charities and other agencies
- whether the short-term funds were efficiently disposed of
- whether the funds were spent on appropriate priorities in a well developed sequence, long term
- whether the most vulnerable people were given priority
- how well all the players worked together
- whether accessible and remote areas were equally well managed
- for the longer term, whether a legal framework for land tenure was established and whether local people were empowered to develop resilience and key features.

Note there are many aspects that could be covered, especially in the context of Park's disaster-response curve, or the Hazard Management Model (before, during and after the hazard event).

> To assess the appropriateness of the response to tsunamis I will look at the Boxing Day tsunami, which was one of the greatest mega disasters of all time, affecting 18 countries of varying levels of development and also because of their location at varied distances from the tsunami centre (see the map) with Aceh in Indonesia the worst hit area as it was beside the epicentre.

Pre-disaster there were a number of factors that influenced the severity of the impact including level of development, standard of governance, population density, degree of sophistication of infrastructure (e.g. the high value Thai resorts filled with foreign tourists) as well the physical nature of the area — lowland coastal plains are particularly vulnerable to tsunami flooding, especially if unprotected by mangroves and coral reefs. Pre-existing strategies for community preparedness and education also increased the potential for mitigation as in Bangladesh.

At the point of disaster impact, physical factors played a huge role in influencing the number of deaths and the degree of damage, with clear distance decay away from the epicentre. The low level of the coral atolls of the Maldives meant they were actually overtopped by tsunami waves, causing much damage. Clearly, further away from the epicentre, the more potential for communication networks to deliver warning. Even so, although in Kenya evacuation plans were carried out, in neighbouring LDC Somali Republic with very poor governance there were significant deaths even though the tsunami waves travelled 5000 km across the ocean, as no warnings were given. So the result of this was that both pre-disaster and impact-wise it was not a level playing field.

e This is a long introduction — is it sufficiently focused?

Short term an Oxfam report recorded that the massive emergency relief effort was tremendously successful in virtually all areas, as there were minimal secondary deaths from starvation or disease epidemics for lack of clean water. Even though temporary schools had to be constructed for 500,000 children by UNICEF, 97% of children returned to school within a month. So in spite of the large scale of deaths (275,000) and the complexity of identifying the 2500 tourists who died in Thailand, emergency relief did the business.

However, the geography of recovery varied considerably. The resilience of communities was dependent on death profiles, the extent of damage and the timelines and effectiveness of assistance. The cohesiveness of a community and the access it had to social, economic and political resources played a critical role in the community's recovery. The biggest single problem was the destruction of infrastructure and communications and meant the multiplicity of NGOs and government organisations lacked planes and boats to reach remote communities.

A year on in the rehabilitation phase again there was differential progress, often between neighbouring communities on the same coast. In Thailand, Phuket was rushed back on to its feet to revive the tourism trade, in contrast to Krabi, which was totally ignored. The Cash for Work Programme was an appropriate scheme, designed to provide work for survivors by rebuilding boats, so they could return to fishing, or desalinating land, so they could return to farming, or craft-working opportunities to replace some of the million lost jobs across southeast Asia.

One big issue was the shortfall between money pledged and money received and used, and the speed it was released for use.

Another issue was the competition between charities and an over-explosion of eye-catching projects such as logo-sponsored fishing boats unsuitable for use.

Longer term progress in re-establishing infrastructure and public services and rebuilding housing has been very slow even after a decade of reconstruction (see Report Boxing Day Tsunami — a decade later). The greatest barrier to progress is problems associated with proving land ownership. In Sri Lanka in a desire to prevent a reoccurrence of the disaster, all houses, including fishermen's, have been built on land behind a buffer zone away from the coast to avoid risk and there have been numerous allegations of corruption. There have been huge arguments about building priorities as the authorities pushed for luxury hotels as opposed to rebuilding homes for local people.

There has been differential spending not only between but within countries.

One appropriate long-term project was the building of the Indian Ocean Tsunami Warning System which should provide warning to avoid tsunami disasters by establishing evacuation routes.

In conclusion, there are questions in many of the countries about the appropriateness of many of the longer term efforts at mitigation and management of tsunamis.

e 6/7 out of 12 marks awarded This student has shown good knowledge of some of the short-term and a few of the long-term responses, but the early part of the answer is of peripheral relevance and the long-term responses are not always brought up to date, so the answer lacks balance.

Band 2 description for AO1 is appropriate, but for AO2 more information is needed. It is a moderate answer.

Indicative content:

Short-term responses include:

- search and rescue for survivors
- assessment of damage and destruction to homes
- provision of food and shelter and emergency accommodation
- first aid and medical provision to address injuries and disease onset
- clearing of infrastructure to allow access, e.g. ports, airports, roads
- water and emergency aid from national governments and international agencies such as the Red Cross and NGOs.

Long-term responses include:

- rebuilding of housing and other infrastructure such as schools and hospitals to move people away from temporary camps
- provision of employment opportunities, for instance new boats for fishermen
- provision of training and education and community preparedness schemes, e.g. tsunami recognition and escape routes
- building of warning systems (Indian Ocean)

- rebuilding and remodelling of coastlines, new natural defences, land use changes in high risk areas, relocating buildings away from coast.

(d) Either:

(i) **Explain why both earthquakes and volcanoes produce tsunamis as secondary hazards.** (14 marks)

Or

(ii) **Explain how physical hazard profiles can be used to compare tectonic hazard events.** (14 marks)

ⓔ To help you answer these questions two essay plans have been produced. A sound and logical structure is essential in essay questions, so careful planning is vital.

(i) Explain why *both* earthquakes and volcanoes (key words, KW) produce tsunamis as secondary hazards (key definitions, KD)	(ii) Explain how physical hazard *profiles* (KD) can be used to compare tectonic hazard events
■ Define secondary hazard ■ Define tsunami as a wave generated by rapid movement of sea bed as a result of tectonic activity ■ Earthquakes involving vertical displacement at a subduction zone cause tsunamis ■ Especially powerful if earthquake focus is shallow and near land ■ Volcanoes cause tsunamis more rarely (5%) after catastrophic eruptions, e.g. Krakatoa 1883 VEI 6 caldera collapse leading to tsunami wave ■ Volcanoes could also generate tsunamigenic landslide	■ Define hazard profile ■ It measures physical characteristics such as magnitude, speed of onset, duration, areal extent, spatial predictability, frequency ■ The comparison can be within categories of earthquakes so earthquake profiles can be compared either with similar magnitudes or just overall profiles to look at social and economic impacts ■ Also the three types of tectonic hazards can be compared to explain, for example, why earthquakes are such killers compared with volcanoes

For (i), exemplar support plus precise explanation will lead to a Band 3 answer. For (ii), exemplar support plus precise details of profiles is vital.

ⓔ It is the explanation of tectonic processes using technical terms and the relevant exemplification which leads to top band answers.

Question 2 (Eduqas style)

To what extent is the quality of governance the most important factor in the recovery of countries and communities from tectonic disasters?

(15 marks: 10 marks AO1, 5 marks AO2)

ⓔ AO1 content encompasses knowledge and understanding as to the importance of good governance as a factor in recovery both nationally (countries) and locally (communities). Knowledge and understanding constitutes two-thirds of the total marks.

For AO2 you must demonstrate application of your knowledge and understanding through an evaluation of the extent to which governance is the most important factor, at both scales in the *recovery* phase from a tectonic disaster.

Student answer

I am going to explain the importance of governance as a means of managing a major tectonic disaster by looking at two tectonic events (Haiti and Christchurch 2010).

First I am going to look at Haiti as an example of bad governance (or I could do Nepal Gorkha earthquake 2015 or even Kashmir).

On January 2010 an earthquake (MM 7.0 so not a huge earthquake) struck the island of Haiti (the poorest LDC in the West). Its epicentre and focus was 25 km west of the capital Port au Prince which had around 2 million people. Clearly something went wrong as over 225,000 people were killed and 60% of buildings were completely destroyed, making around 20% of Haiti's total people (around 1.8 million) homeless so there were about 2 million earthquake refugees who had to be housed in around 1300 squatter camps.

The initial response was dreadful as the port was destroyed and the airport closed because of the damage so they couldn't get emergency supplies in. The government failed to prioritise relief flights and there was a huge delay delivering emergency aid, some had to come in via the Dominican Republic which is at the other end of the island it shares with Haiti.

The real problem was that Haiti was such a poor country, as long-term social problems (no jobs) made the problems much worse. Haiti had had years of complete dictatorship (e.g. Papa and Baby Doc) and since 2006 a weak democracy which did nothing. The UN were already in Haiti trying to overcome the poverty (80% of Haitians were below the poverty line of $2 a day) and the earthquake scored a direct hit on their Haiti HQ and killed a lot of their employees. So there really was nobody in charge in the immediate emergency and the international aid and help was slow to get there (as explained earlier). In all fairness to Haiti, the earthquake was concentrated in the capital where 75% consists of urban slums. These urban slums were inadequately built and all the buildings collapsed so rescue efforts just couldn't get inside them and pre-earthquake 60% of the people didn't have access to toilets or piped water so there was bound to be a problem with disease — so it was all a desperate situation as shown on television programmes. They had to remove 19 million tonnes of rubble before they could start rebuilding.

Also during the recovery period there were further hazards (multi-hazard hot spot) such as cyclones and flooding and landslides from the deforestation of slopes. Then there was the cholera outbreak two years on which killed another 10,000 people in the camps, supposedly brought in by the Nepalese who were part of the UN recovery help force.

Haiti seven years later is limping in its recovery in spite of one or two good local schemes. There are huge disputes as to land ownership (no records or all destroyed in the earthquake).

Whether they will 'build back better' (UN Sendai framework 2015) is doubtful as the government is so bad. Maybe some of the NGO schemes in selected streets of the capital will work.

In my second example, Christchurch, New Zealand Darfield earthquake 2010 (7.1 MM) and Christchurch CBD aftershock 2011 (6.3 MM) does show the benefit of good governance. There were no deaths in the first one at Darfield and only 181 in the second in two large buildings and a bus! It was the second earthquake epicentre 5 km from Christchurch CBD which caused all the problems with 50% of the buildings redlined for demolition largely because of the huge amount of ground shaking (shallow earthquake) and liquefaction.

The emergency rescue operations were amazingly good with a good disaster rescue system and well organised and well-coordinated emergency management, although the mobile phone systems suffered meltdown as everyone rang up to see if their loved ones were safe.

Longer term, there were huge problems with 70,000 residents leaving the city, largely to suburbs and 50,000 people leaving their jobs (leading to raised unemployment except in demolition and rebuilding). Christchurch shopping centre and tourist trade was hit very hard with the temporary closure of many stores and hotels and the loss of port facilities for cruise ships at Lyttleton. Also buildings like the beautiful cathedral were destroyed. However, recovery and re-planning is going on at a great pace with renewal of 100+ km of water mains, 400 km of sewers and 1000 km of roads, also the traffic light system of buildings, red for demolition, amber for repair and retrofitting and green for repair grants has worked very well.

Huge progress is being made, with the revival of the shopping centre using old shipping containers and the rebuilding of facilities such as hotels and the new cardboard cathedral. And long term there is a major scheme to rebuild back Christchurch better which is working really well with plans for a redesigned CBD. Also the various Earthquake Commissions have been created to settle insurance claims and CERA to provide new homes for those who lost them have made remarkable progress.

So here good government provides a model example of a recovery that works as NZ is a well developed country, even if the damage figures were around NZ$130 billion.

So this tale of two earthquakes shows how important good governance can be, even if there are other factors. And it was not all perfect in Christchurch pre-earthquake as some authorities had flouted building regulations and also the geological survey had not made good maps as to where the fault and therefore areas of high earthquake risk were.

e 6/7 out of 15 marks awarded The strategy of comparing two earthquakes is really rather basic. A good plan with why governance is so important, giving multiple examples, would produce a more analytical response. Nonetheless the examples are factually sound and it is possible to award some AO1 credit. The big issue is the very descriptive style of 'whatever comes next' and the poor standard of English expression. There is mention of other factors, but the answer has to remain in the bottom band as there is limited explanation of these other factors and no real reference to countries and communities. In these long questions, sustained and detailed argument is very important.

A possible mark would be AO1 — low Band 2 (4/5 marks), and AO2 — Band 1 (1/2 marks).

Remember that you need both knowledge and understanding, and an evaluation of the question across the full range of tectonic hazards. For example, earthquakes are much less predictable than either volcanoes or tsunamis, or it is much easier to develop scales for magnitude of earthquakes (Richter, MM and Mercalli) than it is for volcanoes (VEI) or tsunamis.

AO1 indicative content:

- Good governance can occur at a variety of scales from the local (community council etc.) to regional, national (whether democratic or autocratic) to international (role of UN and NGOs such as International Red Cross/Red Crescent or Oxfam).
- Good governance is vital in managing the hazard before the event (drills, evacuation routes, monitoring), during the disaster (emergency action), and in the recovery and rehabilitation in the post-disaster phase. It can direct, manage and coordinate in a non-corrupt way and recognise the need for outside help.
- The need for governance can be related to the nature of the disaster in terms of location and scale. The longer and more serious the disaster the greater the need for good governance. Localised disasters are more easily managed.
- Other factors could include the physical profile of the disaster, clearly magnitude is very important, and human factors such as the location of the disaster (accessibility, population density), the level of development as well as the type of governance.
- Useful examples for 'bad' governance could include Nepal and Haiti, or for 'good' governance, possibly Chile, China (Sichuan) or Japan (Tohoku).

For AO2, relevant responses might include the following:

- The relative importance of the other factors such as the physical profile of the hazard (magnitude, speed of onset, duration) and other geographical factors such as location, population density and, above all, level of development which may be related to quality and style of governance.
- The extent to which quality of governance varies in importance in different tectonic events.
- The extent to which government quality can change over time, or vary across a large country such as India or Indonesia.
- The application of quality governance as an issue in well selected examples.

Question 3 (WJEC style)

This question corresponds to section A of Unit 4.

Assess the importance of plate tectonics in understanding the distribution of earthquakes. (6 marks AO1, 13 marks AO2, 1 mark AO3)

ⓔ These long questions require you to demonstrate your ability to develop a sustained line of reasoning that is coherent, relevant and logically structured — so quality of English is *very* important. The greatest proportion of marks are given for AO2, so you must make sure that you apply your knowledge and understanding of the processes that lead the earthquakes.

Student answer

The USGS estimates that several million earthquakes occur each year, with the vast majority of minor significance. There is an inverse relationship between frequency and magnitude with approximately 15 earthquakes a year of MM 7+ and around 130 of MM 6–6.9.

The movement of tectonic plates causes pressure to build up in the Earth's crust. When the pressure is released a series of tremors known as earthquakes occur.

Consequently the global distribution of earthquakes is related to the location of plate boundaries, with around 85% of all earthquakes being related to plate movements at their margins (inter-plate earthquakes). The intense shaking motion, i.e. an earthquake, only lasts for a few seconds. The plane of rupture is called a fault and the location of the movement is the hypocentre or the focus.

The depth of focus which determines the amount of surface damage can be classified as follows:

Shallow focus: 0–70 km, intermediate focus: 70–300 km, and deep focus: 300–700 km. Shallow focus earthquakes account for over 70% of all earthquakes.

At constructive (divergent) plate boundaries, magma pushes up the crust to form ridge and rift features, i.e. mid-ocean ridge, allowing gravitational force to slide the lithosphere away by a process known as ridge push. Transform faults along the ridges cause offsetting which leads to frequent minor earthquakes. This can also occur along the continental divergent boundary along the East African Rift Valley, for example the recent Tanzanian earthquake MM 5.4, 2016.

So called collision boundaries such as those along the Alpine-Himalayan mountain belt also experience frequent, shallow earthquakes, largely because of thrust faulting in the compressed rocks so resulting in interior mountain ranges experiencing earthquakes (Nepal Gorkha 2015).

The most frequent earthquakes are experienced along all types of destructive boundaries as a result of the subduction of oceanic plates by the process of slab pull, a key driver of plate movement. These earthquakes occur in a narrow zone called the Benioff zone with foci ranging from shallow to deep as the oceanic plates are subducted underneath the continental plates. In western

South America the Nazca plate is subducted beneath the South American plate, leading to the frequent occurrence of powerful earthquakes in countries such as Ecuador (2016), Peru (2011) and Chile.

The last type of plate boundary — conservative — leads to high magnitude earthquakes as two plates move laterally with each other, jostling past each other, as with the San Andreas Valley in California. The 'big one', which can be partially explained by gap theory, can occur when the plates get 'stuck' and large-scale pressures are released. Haiti 2010 was formed as a result of localised movement at a conservative boundary. Thus it can be seen that there are a variety of earthquakes (inter-plate) all caused by movements at plate boundaries, with a distinctive spatial geography — some 85% of all earthquakes.

However, there are many causes of intra-plate earthquakes not caused by plate marginal activity.

In Hawaii and the Galapagos, hot spot activity occurs as plumes move upwards leading to huge shield volcanoes. Some earthquake activity in islands such as Hawaii can be associated with volcanic activity.

Equally, in many areas of the world not on plate boundaries, earthquakes can be relatively common, although normally they are of low magnitude. Parts of interior USA such as New Madrid, Missouri, have experienced a number of earthquakes, likely to be associated with movement along old fault lines. Equally, in the UK there are numerous earth tremors and earthquakes around MM 3–4 where movement occurs along former faults, such as the Church Stretton fault which caused earthquakes in Shropshire.

A growing number of earthquakes are associated with human activities. Nuclear explosions such as the recent ones in North Korea have led to significant earth tremors. Moreover, the building of huge dams, such as the Three Gorges Dam in China, hold back huge weights of water in the very large reservoirs. Some scientists argue the increase in the number of earthquakes in Sichuan is linked to this. The Killari earthquake in India is another intra-plate earthquake linked to dam building. A recent controversy is fracking for gas and oil which certainly causes many low magnitude earthquakes such as in eastern USA. The concern is raised as a frequent argument against developing fracking activity such as in Lancashire.

In conclusion therefore, plate boundaries are of fundamental importance in explaining the distribution of earthquakes, especially high magnitude ones, but there is a wide variety of causes — around 15% of earthquakes result from other causes.

e 19/20 marks awarded: 6 marks AO1, 12 marks AO2, 1 mark AO3 This is a well informed and exemplified answer with good up-to-date knowledge of plate tectonics, which deserves Band 3 marks for AO1. The candidate also attempted to analyse the distribution and link to plate movements with a thorough and coherent analysis, so scoring well in AO2. The answer was also well written with sustained, detailed argument, so the 1 mark for AO3 is awarded.

Indicative content:

A01 encompasses knowledge and understanding of the distribution of earthquakes.

- The crust of the Earth is mobile so there is a slow build-up of stress with rocks; when the pressure is suddenly released, parts of the surface experience intense shaking, i.e. an earthquake.
- The global distribution of earthquakes is closely related to plate boundaries, i.e. inter-plate earthquakes.
- At constructive plate boundaries (divergence) shallow focus earthquakes occur at transform faults which cause offsetting at the mid-oceanic ridges — Mid-Atlantic and Mid-Indian Ocean ridges — and also along the continental divergence zone of the East African Rift Valley.
- Shallow focus earthquakes can also occur at collisional plate boundaries on the Alpine–Himalayan belt where orogenies are taking place.
- Strong earthquakes can occur at conservative plate margins where two plates move laterally and jostle past each other — in California on the San Andreas fault.
- Earthquakes can occur at destructive (convergent) plate boundaries and their force varies from shallow to deep along the Benioff zone as slab pull drags one plate beneath another (the oceanic crust is subducted beneath the continental crust — Andean belt).
- They occur at hotspots such as Hawaii associated with volcanic activity caused by a rising plume.
- They also occur along old fault lines, such as those in Madrid in southern USA or those minor earthquakes in the UK (20–30 times a year) strong enough to be felt.
- Earthquakes can be induced by human activity, for example by the weight placed on the Earth's surface by the building of huge reservoirs — a possible cause of the Killari earthquake in India.
- Low magnitude earthquakes are also associated with the process of fracking for oil and gas, for example in eastern USA, and are a major concern in all proposed areas such as Lancashire, UK.
- Earthquakes can result from nuclear bomb explosions, as in North Korea.

For A02 you need to demonstrate application of knowledge and understanding through an overall analysis of the distribution of types of earthquakes (magnitude on MM scale and depth).

- Analysis could involve an attempt to quantify the number of inter-plate to intra-plate earthquakes — 85:15%.
- You could also look at earthquakes from natural causes versus growing numbers caused by human activity.
- Your analysis could also be related to depth of earthquake, which in turn affects the magnitude and impact of an earthquake.
- You will need to provide details of distribution of various examples.
- Analysis should show good understanding as to how plate tectonics actually causes earthquakes using modern theory (slab pull etc.).
- Answers should be summarised in a simple evidence-based conclusion for maximum marks.

Knowledge check answers

1 Firn is partially compacted névé, a type of snow left over from past seasons and recrystallised into a substance denser than the original snow — the intermediate stage between snow and glacier ice.

2 An open system is one that regularly exchanges feedback with its external environment so it has no precise boundary. The balance of inputs, flows, stores and outputs is variable and influenced by external factors such as climate.

3 The cumulative net balance is the total loss or gain of glacier mass over time.

4 Thermohaline circulation, also called the global ocean conveyor belt, is part of the large-scale ocean circulation system driven by ocean density gradients created by surface heat and fresh water fluxes.

5 Proxy data are those data gathered from sources other than instrumental measurement of climate change, such as paintings, literature or natural records of climate, e.g. size of annual tree rings.

6 A group of glaciers chosen by USGS to represent a variety of regimes in continental USA to monitor the impact of climate change. Standardised field and research methodologies are used to make comparisons.

7 Location: cold-based/polar glaciers occur in high latitude regions; warm-based/temperate glaciers occur in high-altitude extra polar regions. Temperature profiles are therefore different (give details). Activity profiles therefore are very different in terms of type of erosional activity at base (give details).

8 In cold-based glaciers there is no basal sliding and internal deformation is the main process. In warm-based glaciers, basal sliding may be dominant although internal deformation and subglacial bed deformation (locally dominant) may occur.

9 The northeast aspect is sheltered, which leads to maximum snow fall accumulation, and is shady, which inhibits the melting of snow, allowing it to collect, so encouraging corrie formation.

10 At a landscape scale the arrangement of landforms can be used from corrie downwards to glaciated troughs. At a meso-scale the profiles of roche moutoneés and crag and tails show the direction of the advance. At a micro-scale striations and gouges are diagnostic, for example striations are orientated parallel to the ice advance with the deepest point of the scratch at the initial point of impact of the debris.

11 Shape — whether features are linear or not; location — where they are found on the valley floor; feature analysis — in terms of size, shape and orientation can also yield 'clues'.

12 By orientation of the feature, e.g. stoss end of drumlins. By deposits behind and in front of terminal moraines. By feature analysis such as the rock type of erratics or the orientation of clasts in boulder clay.

13 Glacial deposits are generally larger calibre, as meltwater streams have less energy for entrainment than do large glaciers and ice sheets. They are unsorted as they are dumped by the ice mass. They are unstratified as they are not sorted into layers by seasonal sediment accumulation. They are more angular as they are not rounded by water contact and attrition.

14 This means that a landform (e.g. eskers, drumlins or tors) can be formed in a number of ways.

15 Their size (width and depth) is dependent on the size of relict ice mass and how fast the infilling takes place.

16 A landform is a specific geomorphological feature, whereas landscape is the resultant scenery produced by an assemblage of landforms in a particular process environment.

17 Certain climatic conditions give rise to distinctive periglacial landscapes formed by frost action, whereas permafrost just refers to permanently frozen ground. Therefore periglacial climate covers a much wider area and set of processes.

18 This is a very slow form of mass movement associated with periglacial areas. The gradual movement of saturated soil down a slope especially where the frozen subsoil (permafrost) acts as a barrier to the percolation of water.

19 List all landforms formed by ground ice formation such as ice lenses, ice wedge polygons, patterned ground and pingos. Also, features such as lobes and terraces from solifluction as well as nivation hollows.

20 A feature resulting from a former periglacial landscape, e.g. at the edge of an ice-covered area in the Ice Age.

21 Disasters involve the realisation of a hazard, so a disaster happens where the avalanche occurs under unexpected weather conditions and suddenly engulfs areas of human settlement or infrastructure, or where humans take part in activities such as cross-country skiing in 'dangerous' areas.

22 Diffluence channels are carved out by trapped glaciers crossing a pre-existing watershed, whereas proglacial spillways are eroded by glacial meltwater.

23 The glaciers are usually only localised in relict landscapes and therefore the landscapes are generally stable and utilised by humans for forestry, farming and tourism with only small areas of glaciers vulnerable to exploitation (see Hohe Tauern case study). In active areas, both glacial and periglacial landscapes are fragile and vulnerable to climate warming and human activities such as tourism.

24 It is renewable and does not give off greenhouse gases as fossil fuels do, although many argue that dam building has a bad effect on the environment.

25 The unique features and flora and fauna can be conserved and protected by regulation and designated protected status or by allowing permit access only to controlled numbers. Activities can be made sustainable, for example ecotourism or organic farming. They can also be made socially and culturally sustainable by involving native communities — see the Hohe Tauern case study.

26 The mantle.

27 African, Eurasian, South American, North American, Pacific, Indo-Australian, Antarctic.

28 a The most violent earthquakes are found at destructive plate boundaries and transform boundaries.

b The most explosive volcanoes are found at destructive plate boundaries or are supervolcanoes associated with continental hotspots.

29 A fault scarp is the initial slope formed by faulting, which is eroded to form a fault line scarp over time.

30 A fold mountain building period.

31 The earthquakes are linked to the disposal of drilling waste water deep underground in disposal wells, not the actual act of drilling. The earthquake occurs when the deep-well disposal of waste water intersects with naturally occurring fault lines.

32 The difference is one of location. When molten rock is still located within the Earth it is known as magma. When molten rock reaches the surface and is extruded, it is known as lava.

33 A smaller earthquake or tremor that follows a major earthquake. In Christchurch, the second earthquake was thought to be an aftershock. Like many other aftershocks it was significant because it occurred in the city centre, so causing huge damage.

34 The theory predicts the relative size and frequency of earthquakes in a given area.

35 Using Tohuku as an example, the primary hazard was the earthquake, the secondary hazard was the tsunami, and the tertiary hazard was the nuclear power station disaster caused by the flooding from the tsunami.

36 An active volcano is a volcano that has had at least one eruption during the past 10,000 years. A dormant volcano is one that is not erupting nor is expected to, but could erupt again in the future as it has in historic times. An extinct volcano has not had an eruption for at least 10,000 years and is not expected to erupt again in a comparable timescale of the future.

37 The volcano had not erupted since 1845 and the eruption was very small scale initially. The disaster was caused by lahars, for which the hazard risk map was prepared but not available. Lahars also hit and rapidly engulfed a large town, Armero, in the middle of the night.

38 The difference lies in location. The focus is the exact point inside the crust of the Earth where the quake begins. The epicentre is the point on the Earth's surface directly above the focus.

39 The earthquake killed many students in schools because of timing and poor building quality. For many families their only child was killed.

40 Certain conditions are required in combination: fault and uplift in coastal zone or nearby ocean; high magnitude (MM6+ earthquake); vertical displacement; shallow focus of earthquake.

41 Almost all events could be chosen, but look for issues of building design, building development in hazard-prone areas or over-confidence that they will be immune from disaster, e.g. Mt Merapi, where people live in a volcanic-prone area.

42 Increased building and higher densities of population within high risk cities, areas often in shanty towns. Deforestation increasing landslide risks after earthquakes. Removal of protective vegetation (mangroves and corals) which protect coastlines from tsunamis.

43 An area in which many hazards (climatic and tectonic) occur within a concentrated area. The one type may exacerbate the other type, e.g. hurricanes and lahars in the Philippines.

44 Possible precursors include any changes from the norm, e.g. small-scale, frequent earthquakes, bulging on the side of the volcano, changes in gas emissions, ground deformation, changes in water temperature of streams.

45 Resilience — toughness, coping capacity and recovery time. Recovery — stages in getting over a disaster, both immediate short term and long term. Rehabilitation — the ability of communities to overcome the psychological upset of a disaster.